WORKBOOK
Teacher's Edition

A Time for Friends

Level 8

Bernard J. Weiss
Eldonna L. Evertts
Loreli Olson Steuer

Holt
Basic
Reading

HOLT, RINEHART AND WINSTON, PUBLISHERS
New York • Toronto • London • Sydney

Copyright © 1980, 1977, 1973 by Holt, Rinehart and Winston, Publishers
All Rights Reserved
Printed in the United States of America

ISBN 0-03-048000-0
90123   111   987654321

Grateful acknowledgment is given to Susan B. Cruikshank, author of Parent Component.

Grateful acknowledgment is given to Annie De Caprio, author of *A Time for Friends, Workbook*, 1977 edition.

Grateful acknowledgment is given to Sheila Martenson, author of *A Time for Friends, Workbook*, 1973 edition.

Cover art by James Endicott.

Table of Contents

Find a word for the sentence.
Write it on the line.

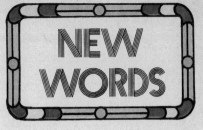
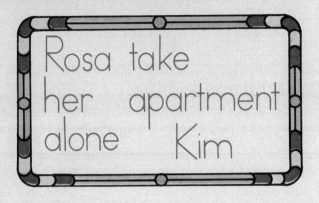

Rosa take
her apartment
alone Kim

1. Kim wanted to go see her friend _____.

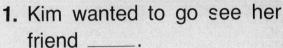

Rosa

2. She was _____ in the apartment.

alone

3. Kim's big sister had to take _____ to see Rosa.

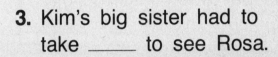

her

4. Mother said that _____ could go alone.

Kim

5. Your sister won't have to _____ you.

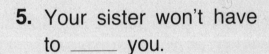

take

6. Kim lived in _____ 17B.

apartment

Level 8: "Kim and Rosa," Part One, pp. 14–19. (Vocabulary)
Objective: To increase a basic reading vocabulary. **Directions:** If necessary, help the children read the directions.
After they have finished the page, have them read the sentences aloud.

1

Long A Vowel Sound

Say these words. Listen for the long a vowel sound.

tail **pail** **game** **make** **save**

Circle the sentence that best tells about the picture.

Brad put water into the pen.

(Brad put water into the pail.)

Brad put water into the pill.

(Fred looked into the cave.)

Fred looked into the can.

Fred looked into the cone.

(Look at the blue paint on Rosa's face.)

Look at the blue pin on Rosa's face.

Look at the blue pan on Rosa's face.

What gum do you want to play?

(What game do you want to play?)

What can do you want to play?

Level 8: "Kim and Rosa," Part One, pp. 14–19. (Decoding/Encoding Skills)
Objective: To associate vowel sounds and symbols in the CVCe and CVVC patterns: /ey/a-e and ai. **Directions:** Have the children say the words and listen for the long a sound. Then have them read the sentences. Have the sentence that describes the picture circled.

Who Has What?

Make each sentence true.
Write the right word on the lines.

frog's   **dog's**   **Kim's**

girl's   **Rosa's**   **mother's**

The girl has a hat.
It is the ____ hat.

Our dog has a bowl.
It is our ____ bowl.

Rosa has a kitten.
It is ____ kitten.

The frog has a house.
It is the ____ house.

Kim has lots of friends.
They are ____ friends.

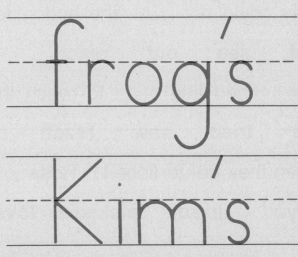

Level 8: "Kim and Rosa," Part One, pp. 14–19. (Language Skills)
Objective: To use 's to show possession. **Directions:** Have the children choose the word that completes each sentence and write it on the line.

3

New Words

elevator	tried	floor
button	reach	picked
	opened	this

These sentences are about "Kim and Rosa."
Circle each word that makes the sentence true.

1. _____ time the elevator went down.

He (This) They It

2. Kim and Rosa got into _____.

(an elevator) a mitten an earmuff a kite

3. Kim could reach the _____ for floor 6.

sheep sign picture (button)

4. Kim got out on floor 6 when the door _____.

asked (opened) picked played

5. Kim lived on _____ 17.

(floor) house country elevator

6. They could not _____ the button for floor 17.

find see put (reach)

7. Kim jumped and _____ to reach the button.

kite (tried) saw reach

8. When they got to floor 17, Rosa _____ up her book.

played liked (picked) loved

Level 8: "Kim and Rosa," Part Two, pp. 15–27. (Vocabulary, Comprehension)
Objectives: To increase a basic reading vocabulary; to recall setting, characters, and events in a selection. **Directions:** Have the children circle the word that fits the sentence that tells about the story.

4

Say the Word

Circle the letter that stands for the beginning sound.

bed
(b) g l

dog
b (d) m

fish
z g (f)

gate
p r (g)

leaf
(l) d s

monkey
b (m) g

nurse
t (n) f

pig
n s (p)

rug
l (r) u

seal
b (s) r

turkey
d v (t)

vest
(v) r p

zipper
(z) v n

tub
s (t) f

bowl
l m (b)

pie
d (p) v

Level 8: "Kim and Rosa," Part Two, pp. 15–27. (Decoding/Encoding Skills)
Objective: To associate consonant sounds and symbols in the initial position: /b/b, /d/d, /f/f, /g/g, /l/l, /m/m, /n/n, /p/p, /r/r, /s/s, /t/t, /v/v, /z/z. **Directions:** The children are to circle the letter that stands for the beginning sound in the picture word.

5

Say the Word

Circle the letter that stands for the sound at the end.

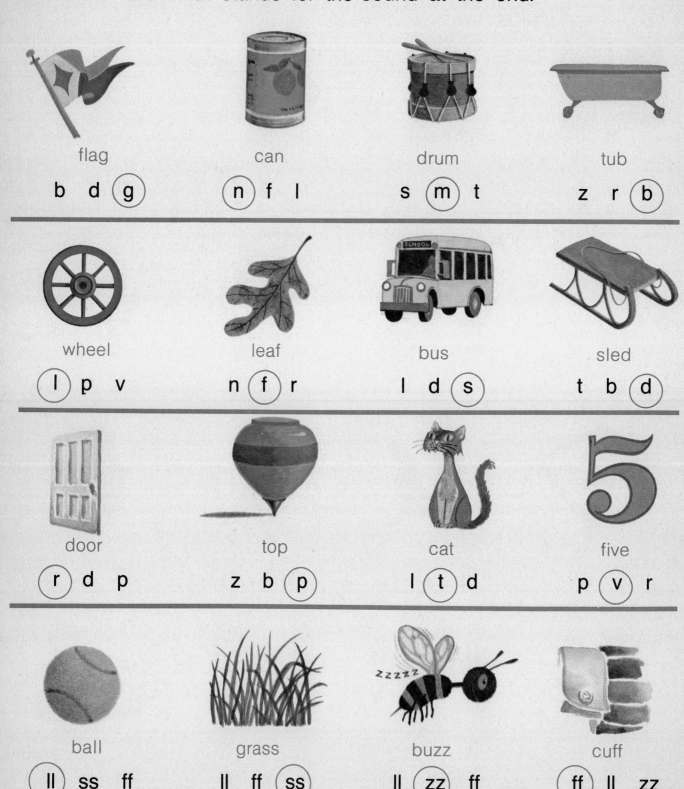

flag	can	drum	tub
b d (g)	(n) f l	s (m) t	z r (b)

wheel	leaf	bus	sled
(l) p v	n (f) r	l d (s)	t b (d)

door	top	cat	five
(r) d p	z b (p)	l (t) d	p (v) r

ball	grass	buzz	cuff
(ll) ss ff	ll ff (ss)	ll (zz) ff	(ff) ll zz

Level 8: "Kim and Rosa," Part Two, pp. 15–27. (Decoding/Encoding Skills)
Objective: To associate consonant sounds and symbols in the final position: /b/b; /d/d; /f/f, ff; /g/g; /l/l, ll; /m/m; /n/n; /p/p; /r/r; /s/s, ss; /t/t; /v/v; /z/z. **Directions:** Give help in naming the pictures. The children are to circle the letter that stands for the final sound in the picture word.

6

Long E Vowel Sound

> Say these words. Listen for the long e vowel sound.
>
> **eat** **read** **bead** **street** **sleep**

Circle the sentence that best tells about the picture.

Fred is saving me a sat.

(Fred is saving me a seat.)

Fred is saving me a set.

Is that a rail flower?

Is that a role flower?

(Is that a real flower?)

Apples have lots of sets.

(Apples have lots of seeds.)

Apples have lots of sails.

Jill picks bands in the morning.

(Jill picks beans in the morning.)

Jill picks books in the morning.

Level 8: "Kim and Rosa," Part Two, pp. 15–27. (Decoding/Encoding Skills)
Objective: To associate the vowel sound /iy/ as in *bead* with the symbols: *ee, ea.* **Directions:** Have the children say the words and listen for the long e sound. Have them read the sentences and circle the one that goes with the picture.

7

Writing Questions

| The pig is sleeping. | Is the pig sleeping? |
| Kim was making cookies. | Was Kim making cookies? |

Make a question from each sentence. Use **is** and **was**.

Rex is a dog.

Is Rex a dog?

It is cold.

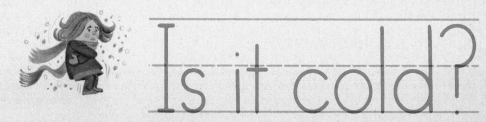

Is it cold?

Ben was eating.

Was Ben eating?

She was reading.

Was she reading?

Level 8: ''Kim and Rosa,'' Part Two, pp. 20–27. (Language Skills)
Objective: To transform statements into questions. **Directions:** Review the example. Point out where **is** and **was** are in both the sentence and question. Then have children write a question from each sentence using the same words.

NEW WORDS

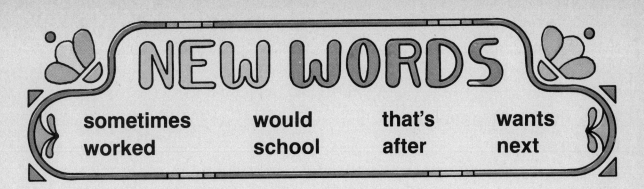

sometimes	would	that's	wants
worked	school	after	next

These sentences are about "Two Friends."
Circle each word that makes the sentence true.

1. _____ Edward and Peter played at Edward's house.

   One   Some   (Sometimes)   Nights

2. The next day they _____ play at Peter's house.

   (would)   see   could   told

3. When they got big, they went to _____.

   fish   (school)   Amy's   Brad's

4. They played and _____ like old friends.

   liked   doing   (worked)   said

5. One day they had cookies. The _____ day they had apples.

   (next)   some   very   much

6. Peter was sick. "_____ too bad," Edward said.

   (That's)   Lots   This   Teddy's

7. _____ school, Edward went home alone.

   Afternoon   Again   (After)   Big

8. Edward's dog _____ him to come home in the afternoon.

   makes   lives   (wants)   reads

Level 8: "Two Friends," Part One, pp. 28–34. (Vocabulary, Comprehension)
Objectives: To increase a basic reading vocabulary; to recall setting, characters and events in a selection. **Directions:** Have the children circle the word that fits the sentence which tells about the story.

9

What Am I?

Circle the right answer.
Then draw me.

I am small.
You can find me in the sky.
I fly from place to place.

Children's Art

I am _____.
a boy (**a bird**) **a bed**

Lots of people live and work in me.
Many people live in my apartments.
My streets have lots of cars on them.

Children's Art

I am _____.
a road **a car** (**a city**)

I can swim in water.
I can sit by a tree.
I jump from place to place.
I eat flies that go by.

Children's Art

I am _____.
a fish (**a frog**) **a pig**

10 **Level 8:** "Two Friends," Part One, pp. 28–34. (Comprehension)
Objective: To identify clues which lead to a conclusion. **Directions:** Have the children read the paragraph and circle the answer. Then have the children draw a picture of what is described in the paragraph.

What's It All About?

Read the story.

Clarita makes new friends.
One new friend is Amy.
Clarita and Amy play games.
Teddy is a new friend, too.
They play with Teddy's dog.
Clarita has lots of new friends.

Check the best topic for the story.

_____puppies   ✔_Clarita's friends   _____Teddy

Check the sentence that tells the main idea.

_____Amy and Clarita play games.

_____Teddy has a dog and three puppies.

_✔_Clarita makes a lot of new friends.

Rosa and Sora like to go in the elevator.
They go up in the elevator to get home.
They go up in the elevator to see Mrs. Gold.
Rosa and Sora go up in the elevator to play games with Peter.

Check the best topic for the story.

_✔_the elevator   _____Mrs. Gold   _____Rosa

Check the sentence that tells the main idea.

_____Mrs. Gold lives in Rosa's apartment house.

_____Rosa and Sora live in an apartment house.

_✔_Rosa and Sora go up and down in the elevator.

Level 8: "Two Friends," Part One, pp. 28–34. (Comprehension)
Objective: To select the main topic and/or idea from several choices. **Directions:** Have the children read the story. Then have them put a check beside the word that is the best topic for the story. Next, have them put a check beside the sentence that tells the main idea.

11

Long O Vowel Sound

Say these words. Listen for the long <u>o</u> sound.

r<u>oa</u>d **c<u>oa</u>t** **n<u>o</u>s<u>e</u>** **n<u>o</u>t<u>e</u>** **b<u>o</u>n<u>e</u>**

Circle the sentence that best tells about the picture.

Kim finds a nut in school.

(Kim finds a note in school.)

Kim finds a not in school.

The cat is sleeping next to Sandy's cot.

The cat is sleeping next to Sandy's cow.

(The cat is sleeping next to Sandy's coat.)

Juan wants the dog's bed.

(Juan wants the dog's bone.)

Juan wants the dog's bad.

Clarita's kitten eats the sand.

(Clarita's kitten eats the soap.)

Clarita's kitten eats the sun.

Level 8: "Two Friends," Part One, pp. 28–34. (Decoding/Encoding Skills)
Objective: To associate vowel sounds and symbols in CVVC and CVCe patterns: /ow/ *oa* and *o-e*. **Directions:** Have the children say the words and listen for the long o sound. Have them read the sentences and then circle the sentence that goes with the picture.

12

These sentences are about "Two Friends."
Circle each word that makes the sentence true.

1. When Peter was sick, Edward said, "That's too ____."

all   happy   good   (bad)

2. Edward said, "Jimmy ____ in the new house."

has   (lives)   swims   sings

3. Jimmy told Edward ____ his cat.

(about)   after   again   then

4. ____ wanted to show Jimmy his dog.

Animal   Brad   (Edward)   Kate

5. Edward said, "Peter ____ a frog."

eats   goes   comes   (has)

6. Peter didn't want to play at ____ house.

(Jimmy's)   Jimmy   Amy's   bird

7. Peter said, "Edward ____ my friend."

didn't   (isn't)   won't   can't

8. Peter said, "____ at Jimmy's house."

His   Here's   (He's)   I'll

Level 8: "Two Friends," Part Two, pp. 28–40. (Vocabulary, Comprehension)
Objectives: To increase a basic reading vocabulary; to recall setting, characters, and events in a selection. **Directions:**
Have the children circle the word that completes a sentence which tells about the story.

13

Long I Vowel Sound

Say these words. Listen for the long <u>i</u> vowel sound.

l<u>i</u>ke   **k<u>i</u>t<u>e</u>**   **n<u>i</u>c<u>e</u>**   **t<u>i</u>m<u>e</u>**   **w<u>i</u>s<u>e</u>**   **wh<u>i</u>t<u>e</u>**

Circle the sentence that best tells about the picture.

(He's got a kite on his bike.)

He's got a kitten on his bike.

He's got a kit on his bike.

There are rip apples in the store.

There are rope apples in the store.

(There are ripe apples in the store.)

(Gus went for a bike ride.)

Gus went for a bike rid.

Gus went for a bike raid.

The bird lives in the pin tree.

(The bird lives in the pine tree.)

The bird lives in the pain tree.

Level 8: "Two Friends," Part Two, pp. 35–40. (Decoding/Encoding Skills)
Objective: To associate vowel sounds and symbols: /ay/i-e as in *ice*. **Directions:** Have the children say the words and listen for the long *i* sound. Then have them read the sentences and circle the one that goes with the picture.

New Words

forgot   walked   walk
forget   without   liking

These sentences are about "Two Friends."
Circle each word that makes the sentence true.

1. Peter had to _____ to school alone.

   walked   **swim**   **be**   (**walk**)

2. But then he _____ with Edward and Jimmy.

   (**walked**)   **asked**   **jump**   **walk**

3. School wasn't _____ for Peter.

   quiet   (**fun**)   **good**   **small**

4. He had to read _____ Edward.

   about   **after**   **with**   (**without**)

5. Peter couldn't _____ what Jimmy said about his frog.

   (**forget**)   **reach**   **jump**   **sing**

6. "_____ you like to see Jimmy's cat?" asked Edward.

   Could   **Are**   (**Would**)   **Wants**

7. Peter _____ about going home.

   forget   **jumped**   (**forgot**)   **did**

8. Peter forgot about not _____ Jimmy.

   looking   (**liking**)   **doing**   **playing**

Level 8: "Two Friends " Part Three, pp. 29–45. (Vocabulary, Comprehension)
Objectives: To increase a basic reading vocabulary; to recall setting, characters, and events in a selection. **Directions:**
Have the children circle the word that completes a sentence about the story.

OO as in Moon

Say these words. Listen for the sound of the letters oo.

moo   **moon**   **school**   **too**   **raccoon**

Circle the sentence that best tells about the picture.

There are my father's tails.

(There are my father's tools.)

There are my father's tops.

Kittens eat lots of fad.

Kittens eat lots of find.

(Kittens eat lots of food.)

Brad puts on his own bats.

Brad puts on his own boats.

(Brad puts on his own boots.)

Juan put the broom on the steal.

(Juan put the broom on the stool.)

Juan put the broom on the stop.

Level 8: "Two Friends," Part Three, pp. 41–45. (Decoding/Encoding Skills)
Objective: To associate vowel sounds and symbols: /uw/oo as in *pool*. **Directions:** Have the children say the words and listen for the sound oo stands for. Then have them read the sentences and circle the one that goes with the picture.

Long U and OO as in Moon

Say these words. Listen for the vowel sound.

too   **m<u>oo</u>n**   **J<u>u</u>n<u>e</u>**   **c<u>u</u>b<u>e</u>**

Circle the sentence that best tells about the picture.

That's a cut puppy.

(That's a cute puppy.)

That's a cat puppy.

This raccoon is had.

This raccoon is hug.

(This raccoon is huge.)

Her toy came out.

(Her tooth came out.)

Her top came out.

Can I eat your car?

Can I end your car?

(Can I use your car?)

Level 8: "Two Friends," Part Three, pp. 41–45. (Decoding/Encoding Skills)
Objective: To associate vowel sounds and symbols: /uw/oo, u-e as in pool; /yuw/u-e as in cute. **Directions:** Have the children say the words and listen for the vowel sound. Then have them read the sentences and circle the one that best describes the picture.

New Words

thank	cousin	asks	telling
fly	help	crab	leg

These sentences are about "That's What Friends Are For."
Circle the word that makes the sentence true.

1. He can't walk on his bad ____.

let (leg) hand long

2. They were all ____ Teddy what to do.

doing looking smelling (telling)

3. Teddy said "____ you" to his friends.

do (thank) look then

4. Teddy wants to go to see his ____.

brother boy (cousin) pig

5. "What can I do?" he ____.

did (asks) looks as

6. A ____ said, "I would walk."

apple burro boy (crab)

7. A bird tells him to ____.

(fly) eat jump love

8. The raccoon said, "You can ____."

tell will hello (help)

Level 8: "That's What Friends Are For," pp. 48–62. (Vocabulary, Comprehension)
Objectives: To increase a basic reading vocabulary; to recall setting, characters, and events in a selection. **Directions:** Have the children circle the word that completes a sentence about the story.

What Is It About?

Read about Teddy.

Lots of friends told Teddy what to do.
His friend the bird told him to fly
to his cousin's house.
The daddy-longlegs told him to walk on lots of legs.
The monkey told him to go from tree to tree.
The crab told him to get a new leg.

Check the best sentence that tells all about Teddy.

_____ The monkey told him to go from tree to tree.
_____ The crab told him to get a new leg.
✔ Lots of friends told Teddy what to do.

Read about Kim and Rosa.

Kim and Rosa went in the elevator
in the apartment house.
Kim went to play with Rosa on floor 6.
Rosa went to play with Kim on floor 17.
They could not walk up and down.
They went up and down in the elevator.

Check the best sentence that tells all about Kim and Rosa.

_____ Kim and Rosa played on floor 6.
✔ Kim and Rosa went in the elevator when they
    went to play.
_____ Kim and Rosa liked to cook.

Level 8: "That's What Friends Are For," pp. 48–62. (Comprehension)
Objective: To identify the main idea of a story when it is explicitly stated. **Directions:** The children check the sentence that gives the main idea of the paragraph.

19

"ck" Words

Say these words. Listen for the last sound.

sick   trick   clock   back

Circle the word that makes a sentence.

1. The bird is on the _____.

   (**track**)   **tree**   **train**

_____

2. Edward forgot where he put his _____.

   claw   **clown**   (**clock**)

_____

3. Kitty put her _____ on her back.

   pat   (**pack**)   **dock**

_____

4. The mother cat will _____ her kittens.

   list   **line**   (**lick**)

_____

5. Do you have my _____?

   (**sock**)   **soap**   **song**

_____

6. The night sky is _____.

   blue   (**black**)   **blot**

20   Level 8: "That's What Friends Are For," pp. 48–61. (Decoding/Encoding Skills)
Objective: To associate a consonant sound and symbols in the final position. **Directions:** Have the children say the words and listen to the ending sound. Then have them circle the correct word to make a sentence.

—ank

Say these words. Listen for the ending sounds.

thank   **bank**   **tank**

Circle the word that completes the sentence.

1. I _____ some water.

blank   tank   (drank)

2. _____ you for the book.

(Thank)   Bank   Tank

3. Write your name on the _____.

plank   sank   (blank)

4. The car slowly _____.

blank   (sank)   plank

5. Do you have fish in your _____?

drank   bank   (tank)

6. Do you see my new _____?

(bank)   blank   back

Level 8: "That's What Friends Are For," pp. 48–61. (Decoding/Encoding Skills)
Objective: To make a sentence by choosing the correct word among several words with the same base but different initial consonants. **Directions:** Have the children say the words and listen to the ending sounds. Then have them circle the correct word to make a sentence.

21

Good Night, Knight!

Read each sentence.
Put a line under the words that sound the same in the two sentences.
Draw a line from the sentence to the matching picture.

Mother makes cookies with <u>flour</u>.

Look at the red <u>flower</u>.

He can jump on his <u>right</u> leg.

I'll <u>write</u> a book about birds.

"<u>Would</u> you go to the store?" asked mother.

The man wanted some <u>wood</u>.

Rosa has a <u>new</u> dress.

Rex <u>knew</u> it.

Level 8: "That's What Friends Are For," pp. 48–61. (Language Skills)
Objective: To distinguish homophones. **Directions:** Have the directions read. If necessary, help the children find the homophones they are to underline. The children are to draw a line from the sentence to the picture it matches.

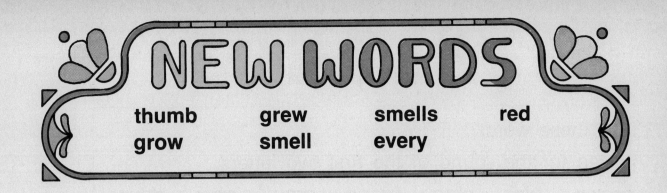

NEW WORDS

thumb   grew   smells   red
grow   smell   every

These sentences are about "The Little Red Flower."
Circle each word that makes the sentence true.

1. No flowers ever _____ in the small town.

(grew)   finds   gets   played

2. One day Mr. Greenthumb put a _____ flower in his window.

right   quiet   happy   (red)

3. The people all said, "That flower _____ good."

swim   read   (smells)   tells

4. But they said, "We can't get flowers to _____."

know   (grow)   could   goes

5. A man said, "His _____ is green."

tail   games   (thumb)   sheep

6. The people came to _____ the flower.

(smell)   grow   stop   fly

7. They came _____ day.

green   bad   new   (every)

Level 8: "The Little Red Flower," Part One, pp. 64–69. (Vocabulary, Comprehension)
Objectives: To increase a basic reading vocabulary; to recall setting, characters, and events in a selection. **Directions:**
Have the children circle the word that fits the sentence.

23

BLENDS

Say these words.
Listen for the sound of the first two letters.

brown **t**rick **c**rab **f**riend **g**row **p**ray **d**river

Circle the word that makes a sentence.

1. Look at the little ____ mouse.

   (**gray**) **tray** **ray**

2. A ____ is a big bird.

   cow **grow** (**crow**)

3. The ____ is next to the tree.

   boom **groom** (**broom**)

4. The apple is on the ____ .

   pray **gray** (**tray**)

5. The ____ is in the brown car.

   (**driver**) **bear** **dive**

6. The ____ is on the ground.

   cog (**frog**) **dog**

Level 8: "The Little Red Flower," Part One, pp. 64–69. (Decoding/Encoding Skills)
Objective: To associate sounds and symbols for consonant blends (clusters) in the initial position: /br/br, /kr/cr, /dr/dr, /fr/fr, /gr/gr, /pr/pr, /tr/tr. **Directions:** Have children say the words and listen for the sound of the first two letters. Then have them circle the correct word to make a sentence.

24

sh or th

Say these words.
Listen for the sound of the underlined letters.
show   **sh**e   fi**sh**   **th**is   **th**umb   wi**th**

Write the missing **th** or **sh**.

1. I will brush my 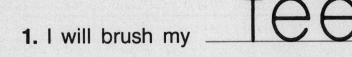 teeth .

2. My dog likes to shake his toys.

3. Did you help wash the car?

4. Open your 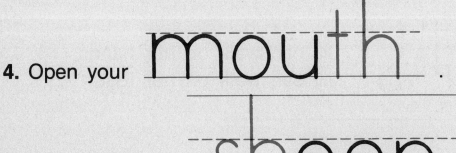 mouth .

5. Jimmy has two sheep .

Level 8: "The Little Red Flower," Part One, pp. 64–69. (Decoding/Encoding)
Objective: To associate consonant sounds and symbols in the initial and final positions: /θ/th as in *thin* (th), /š/sh as in *she*. **Directions:** Have the children say the words and listen for the sound of **sh** and **th**. Then have them read the sentence and write the missing *th* or *sh*.

25

USING and

Jay has a cat.
Jay has a dog.

Jay has a cat and a dog.

The boy likes to read.
The girl likes to read.

The boy and the girl like to read.

Jill can walk on her hands.
Jill can walk on her feet.

Jill can walk on her hands and on

her feet.

Level 8: "The Little Red Flower," Part One, pp. 64–69. (Vocabulary, Language Skills)
Objectives: To increase a basic reading vocabulary; to identify the use of *and*. **Directions:** The children read each pair of sentences for the picture. They then combine the two sentences to make one sentence by writing the missing words.

26

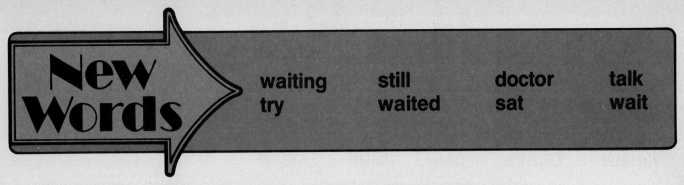

New Words

waiting	still	doctor	talk
try	waited	sat	wait

These sentences are about "The Little Red Flower."
Circle the word that makes the sentence true.

1. A man went in to _____ to Mr. Greenthumb.

walk   wait   (talk)   trap

2. The man told the boy to _____ by the window.

play   wish   want   (wait)

3. The people _____ to find out about Mr. Greenthumb.

(waited)   walked   wouldn't   worked

4. The man went to find a _____.

friend   (doctor)   elevator   cousin

5. Lots of people were _____ by the window.

helping   liking   (waiting)   playing

6. The people were _____ by the window when the doctor came.

not   (still)   after   green

7. A boy said he would _____ to save the flower.

(try)   stop   reach   walk

8. All night the boy _____ by the flower.

played   worked   (sat)   grew

Level 8: "The Little Red Flower," Part Two, pp. 70–76. (Vocabulary, Comprehension)
Objectives: To increase a basic reading vocabulary; to understand the direct, literal meaning of a sentence; to recall setting, characters, and events in a selection. **Directions:** Have the children circle the word that completes a sentence about the story.

BLENDS

Say these words.
Listen for the sound of the first two letters.

flower   **Clarita**   **play**   **blue**   **sleep**

Circle the word that makes a sentence.

1. Dan is in the school _____.

   clay   pay   (play)

_____

2. My friend lives on the next _____.

   (block)   flock   clock

_____

3. The _____ is red, white, and blue.

   slap   (flag)   clap

_____

4. There is a goldfish in my _____.

   class   place   (glass)

_____

5. I made an animal out of _____.

   tray   (clay)   play

_____

6. Do you see my new _____?

   bed   (sled)   bread

Level 8: "The Little Red Flower," Part Two, pp. 70–76. (Decoding/Encoding Skills)
Objective: To associate sounds and symbols for consonant blends (clusters) in the initial position: /bl/bl/, /kl/cl/, /fl/fl/, /gl/gl/, /pl/pl/, /sl/sl/. **Directions:** Have children say the words and listen for the sound of the first two letters. Then have them circle the correct word to make a sentence.

Short and Long

Circle the sentence that best tells about the picture.

My friend and I go to the sum doctor.

My friend and I go to the same doctor.

My friend and I go to the sand doctor.

I make my bead in the morning.

I make my band in the morning.

I make my bed in the morning.

She picked the reed flowers.

She picked the red flowers.

She picked the road flowers.

Did you eat that cone of beans?

Did you eat that cane of beans?

Did you eat that can of beans?

Level 8: "The Little Red Flower," Part Two, pp. 70–76. (Decoding/Encoding Skills)
Objective: To distinguish between words with short vowels and words with long vowels by choosing the sentence that best describes the picture. **Directions:** Have children circle the sentence that best tells about the picture.

29

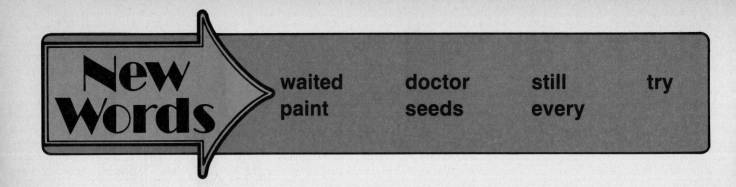

New Words

waited   doctor   still   try
paint   seeds   every

These sentences are about "The Little Red Flower."
Circle each word that makes the sentence true.

1. With Mr. Greenthumb's help, the _____ grew.

   water   bowl   signs   (seeds)

2. The people _____ after the doctor went into the house.

   (waited)   thanks   wanted   lives

3. A boy said he would _____ to save the flower.

   see   (try)   paint   talk

4. The _____ said he could not save the flower.

   Mr. Greenthumb   **frog**   **(doctor)**   **cousin**

5. When Mr. Greenthumb came out, the flower was _____ there.

   here   **not**   **(still)**   **about**

6. Mr. Greenthumb said there was _____ on his thumb.

   place   **water**   **room**   **(paint)**

7. Now there is a flower in _____ window in town.

   all   **alone**   **(every)**   **new**

Level 8: "The Little Red Flower," Part Three, pp. 64–83 (Vocabulary, Comprehension)
Objectives: To increase a basic reading vocabulary; to recall setting, characters, and events in a selection. **Directions:** The children circle the word that fits the sentence.

30

What Do They Do Next?

Read about Jay and his mother.

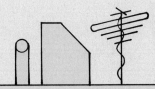

Jay and his mother live in the city.
When she goes to the store, Jay goes with her.
They go out of their apartment.
They go down in the elevator and out to the street.
They walk into the store.
His mother gets lots of fish, beans, and apples to eat.
Then Jay has some to take home.
And his mother has some to take home.
They walk out of the store.

A. What was first? next? last?
Write 1, 2, or 3 on the line to show the order.

_3_ They got fish, beans, and apples.
_1_ They went out of their apartment.
_2_ They went to the store.

B. What do they do then? Check the best ending.
____ Then Jay and his mother get into their car.
____ Then Jay and his mother go fishing.
_✓_ Then Jay and his mother go home.

Level 8: "The Little Red Flower," Part Three, pp. 64–83. (Comprehension)
Objective: To predict what may happen next in a selection. **Directions:** A. The children are to write numbers on the line to show the order of the sentences. B. The children are to predict outcomes by checking the sentence that shows what might have happened next.

Short and Long O

 box

 soap

Say these words. Listen for the short o sound. **not stop got**	Say these words. Listen for the long o sound. **coat note nose**

Read the sentence.
Listen to the vowel sound in the underlined word.
Circle the **S** if the vowel sound is short.
Circle the **L** if the vowel sound is long.

1. Button up your coat.   S   (L)

2. She is sleeping on the cot.   (S)   L

3. Do you play jump rope in school?   S   (L)

4. The cat ran to the top of the tree.   (S)   L

5. I eat toast in the morning.   S   (L)

6. We rode in a big brown car.   S   (L)

7. I saw the smoke from the fire.   S   (L)

8. They laughed at my joke.   S   (L)

9. Who has my fishing rod?   (S)   L

10. We are not going home.   (S)   L

Level 8: "The Little Red Flower," Part Three, pp. 77–83. (Decoding/Encoding Skills)
Objective: To identify words with long or short vowel sounds. **Directions:** Have children read each sentence and think of the vowel sound in the underlined word. Have them circle the S if the vowel sound is short. Have them circle the L if the vowel sound is long.

Long O Vowel Sound

Circle the sentence that best tells about the picture.

The raise smells so good.

The rose smells so good. ⟵ (circled)

The rat smells so good.

Kim has a new robe. ⟵ (circled)

Kim has a new rob.

Kim has a new rode.

He can climb to the top of the pail.

He can climb to the top of the pool.

He can climb to the top of the pole. ⟵ (circled)

Jim laughed at Jill's tone.

Jim laughed at Jill's job.

Jim laughed at Jill's joke. ⟵ (circled)

This rod will take you home.

This road will take you home. ⟵ (circled)

This raid will take you home.

Level 8: "The Little Red Flower," Part Three, pp. 77–83. (Decoding/Encoding Skills)
Objective: To identify words with a long *o* sound by selecting a sentence that goes with the picture. **Directions:**
Have the children read the sentences. Have the sentence that describes the picture circled.

WRITING QUESTIONS

He picks flowers.	Does he pick flowers?
She picked a flower.	Did she pick a flower?

Make a question from each sentence. Use *did* and *does*.

1. Peter walks alone.

Does Peter walk alone?

2. Jim walked alone.

Did Jim walk alone?

3. He saved the flower.

Did he save the flower?

4. He waters the flower.

Does he water the flower?

Level 8: "The Little Red Flower," Part Three, pp. 64–83. (Language Skills)
Objectives: To transfer statements into questions. **Directions:** Review the example. Point out the changes made in verb form, in word order, or by addition of a word. Have children write a question from each sentence using the same words.

How Many Do You Know?

Circle the word your teacher reads.

floor	worked	that's	(he's)
forgot	(next)	(thumb)	help
(fun)	new	telling	her
fly	nights	try	helping
Rosa	after	school	sat
(reach)	about	(sometimes)	still
talk	(asks)	sat	(seeds)
red	alone	smell	save
(every)	little	opened	grow
elevator	liking	(cousin)	green
eat	leg	crab	walk
isn't	(lives)	cousin's	(grew)
(their)	(brothers)	would	forgot
talk	doctor	without	(flower)
thank	buttons	(walked)	forget
tried	bad	waiting	floor

Level 8: "The Little Red Flower," Part Three, pp. 77–83 (Comprehension)
Objective: To increase a basic reading vocabulary. **Directions:** Pronounce the word circled in the Teacher's Edition. Use the word in a sentence and then pronounce it again. The children are to circle the word in their books. For an optional extended test, pronounce each underlined word. The circled and underlined words are high frequency words.

35

Why?

Check the best ending to each sentence.

1. Maggie got Ellen's old clothes because

_✓_ Ellen got too big for her clothes.

_____ Mike got too big for his clothes.

2. Maggie had to sleep in Ellen's room because

_____ Ellen asked her to sleep in her room.

_✓_ Mike had to have his own room.

3. Maggie couldn't play with Mike because

_____ Mike was too big to play with her.

_✓_ Mike was too little to play with her.

4. Maggie couldn't play with Ellen because

_____ Maggie was too big to play with Ellen.

_✓_ Maggie was too little to play with Ellen.

5. Maggie was unhappy because

_✓_ she was in the middle.

_____ she was too big.

Level 8: "Maggie in the Middle," Part One. pp. 88–92. (Comprehension)
Objective: To recognize causes when they are explicitly stated. **Directions:** Have children put a check next to the ending that best completes the sentence.

Say the Word

Circle the missing letter or letters.

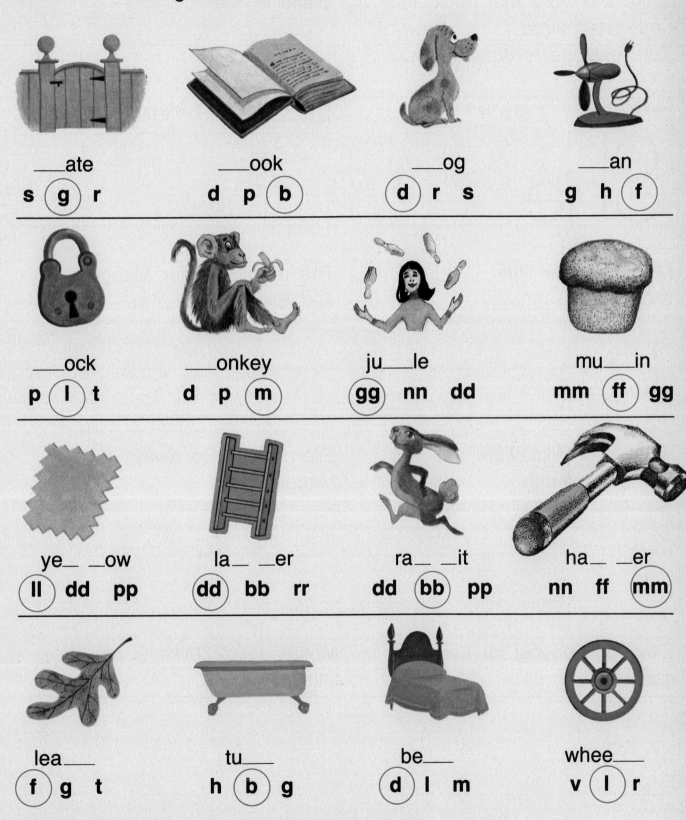

___ate
s **(g)** **r**

___ook
d **p** **(b)**

___og
(d) **r** **s**

___an
g **h** **(f)**

___ock
p **(l)** **t**

___onkey
d **p** **(m)**

ju___le
(gg) **nn** **dd**

mu___in
mm **(ff)** **gg**

ye_ _ow
(ll) **dd** **pp**

la_ _er
(dd) **bb** **rr**

ra_ _it
dd **(bb)** **pp**

ha_ _er
nn **ff** **(mm)**

lea___
(f) **g** **t**

tu___
h **(b)** **g**

be___
(d) **l** **m**

whee___
v **(l)** **r**

Level 8: "Maggie in the Middle," Part One, pp. 88–92. (Decoding/Encoding Skills)
Objective: To associate consonant sounds and symbols in the initial, medial, and final positions: /b/b, bb; /d/d, dd; /f/f, ff; /g/g, gg; /l/l, ll; /m/m, mm. **Directions:** Tell the children that a consonant may be missing at the beginning, middle, or end of the word for the picture. Demonstrate the procedure by writing *girl, waffle,* and *rub* on the board and circling the *g, ff,* and *b*.

37

She He It They

Write the word that could take the place of the underlined word.
The first one is done for you.

Maggie had a big sister.

She

The clothes fit Maggie.

They

Mike was her little brother.

He

The room was for Maggie and Ellen to sleep in.

It

Ellen and Mike were not fun to play with.

They

Ellen said, "Go away, Maggie."

She

Ellen got too big for her clothes.

She

Mother said, "Mike is too little to play."

He

Level 8: "Maggie in the Middle," Part One, pp. 88–92. (Language Skills)
Objective: To substitute a pronoun for the noun or noun phrase in the subject of a sentence. **Directions:** The children substitute a pronoun for the noun in each sentence, using the words in the title.

One Word For Two

| You will   You'll |
| They will   They'll |

| She will   She'll |
| We will   We'll |

| He will   He'll |
| I will   I'll |

Write the word that takes the place of the underlined words.

1. They will go to school.
_____ go to school.

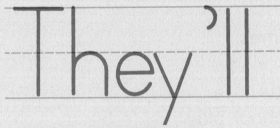

4. She will make cookies.
_____ make cookies.

2. You will have fun.
_____ have fun.

5. He will like the toy.
_____ like the toy.

3. We will see the rabbit.
_____ see the rabbit.

6. I will see a monkey.
_____ see a monkey.

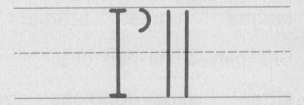

Level 8: ''Maggie in the Middle,'' Part One, pp. 88–92. (Language Skills)
Objective: To use the contractions of *will*. **Directions:** Have the children review the contractions and the two words that each contraction is made from. Have the children read the directions. Then have them read the first sentence in each pair, noting the underlined word. Using the teaching frame as a reference, the children should then write the corresponding contractions on the line.

39

New Words → middle   away   part   stage
clothes   kangaroo   noon   jumps

These sentences are about "Maggie in the Middle."
Circle each word that makes the sentence true.

1. Maggie was too big for Mike and too little

   for Ellen, so she was in the _____.

   room   (middle)   tryouts   stage

2. She had to have Ellen's old _____.

   doctor   can   (clothes)   house

3. Mike ran _____ with Maggie's games.

   (away)   still   about   after

4. Maggie wanted a _____ in the school play.

   seeds   paint   (part)   park

5. She wanted to be on the _____.

   stop   clothes   store   (stage)

6. Maggie went to see Mrs. Chang at _____.

   home   (noon)   night   Mrs. Cook's

7. She did big and little _____.

   laughs   (jumps)   brothers   legs

8. She played the part of a _____.

   kitten   daddy-longlegs   raccoon   (kangaroo)

Level 8: "Maggie in the Middle," Part Two, pp. 93–98. (Vocabulary, Comprehension)
Objectives: To increase a basic reading vocabulary; to recall setting, characters, and events in a selection. **Directions:**
The children circle the word that fits the sentence.

40

How About Now?

Say these words.
Listen for the sound the letters <u>ow</u> and <u>ou</u> stand for.
mouth   down   cow   brown   house

Write a word to make a sentence.

1. Did a fly go in the _house_ ?

2. Open your _mouth_ .

3. She wants a _brown_ mouse.

4. Does a _cow_ live in a house?

5. He jumped _down_ .

Level 8: ''Maggie in the Middle,'' Part Two, pp. 93–98. (Decoding/Encoding Skills)
Objective: To associate the vowel sounds and symbols: /aw/ou, ow as in *about* and *cow*. **Directions:** Say the words with the children. Then have the children write the missing word on the line.

Say the Word

Say the word for each picture.
Circle the missing letter or letters.

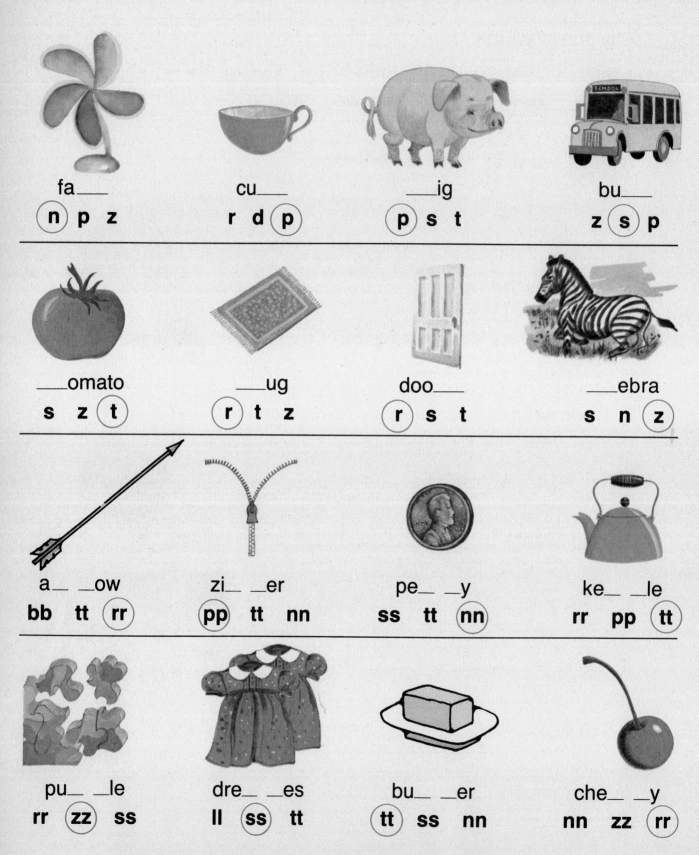

fa___
(n) p z

cu___
r d (p)

___ig
(p) s t

bu___
z (s) p

___omato
s z (t)

___ug
(r) t z

doo___
(r) s t

___ebra
s n (z)

a___ ___ow
bb tt (rr)

zi___ ___er
(pp) tt nn

pe___ ___y
ss tt (nn)

ke___ ___le
rr pp (tt)

pu___ ___le
rr (zz) ss

dre___ ___es
ll (ss) tt

bu___ ___er
(tt) ss nn

che___ ___y
nn zz (rr)

Level 8: "Maggie in the Middle," Part Two, pp. 88–98. (Decoding/Encoding Skills)
Objective: To associate consonant sounds and symbols in the initial, medial and final positions: /n/n, nn; /p/p, pp;
/r/r, rr; /s/s, ss; /t/t, tt; /z/z, zz. **Directions:** Tell the children that the consonant sound may appear in the beginning,
end, or middle of the word. Then encourage the children to proceed independently.

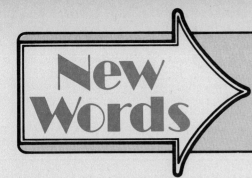

New Words

everyone   helped   care   being

jumping   called   over

These sentences are about "Maggie in the Middle."
Circle each word that makes the sentence true.

1. Maggie did not like ____ in the middle.

   looking   reading   (being)   doing

2. Mrs. Chang ____ Maggie.

   jumped   stopped   laughed   (helped)

3. Mrs. Chang told her to go ____ about on the stage.

   waiting   sing   helping   (jumping)

4. Maggie ____ out, "I'm the green kangaroo."

   (called)   helped   asks   finds

5. She jumped all ____ the stage.

   after   again   still   (over)

6. She liked the ____ of the kangaroo.

   paint   bench   (part)   road

7. ____ liked the play.

   One   She   Two   (Everyone)

8. Now Maggie did not ____ that she was in the middle.

   (care)   help   being   jumps

Level 8: "Maggie in the Middle," Part Three, pp. 99–105. (Vocabulary, Comprehension)
Objectives: To increase a basic reading vocabulary; to recall setting, characters, and events in a selection. **Directions:** The children circle the word that makes the sentence true.

Abbreviations

Write the abbreviation for each word.
Choose from the abbreviations in the box.

Ave.	Dr.	Dec.	St.
Mr.	Sat.	E.	Mrs.

Mister

Mr.

Mistress

Mrs.

East

E.

Street

St.

December

Dec.

Saturday

Sat.

Doctor

Dr.

Avenue

Ave.

Level 8: "Maggie in the Middle," Part Three, pp. 99–105. (Study Skills)
Objective: To use abbreviations. **Directions:** Help the children read the directions. Then encourage them to work independently.

FILES

Each shelf has a part of the alphabet.

Each drawer has a part of the alphabet.
Write the letter or letters that are missing.
Go from the front of the drawer to the back.

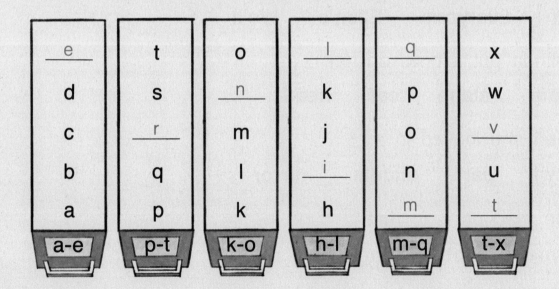

Level 8: ''Maggie in the Middle,'' Part Three, pp. 88–105. (Study Skills)
Objective: To supply a letter of the alphabet that is missing from a sequence. **Directions:** The children write the letter or letters that are missing from the alphabetical sequence.

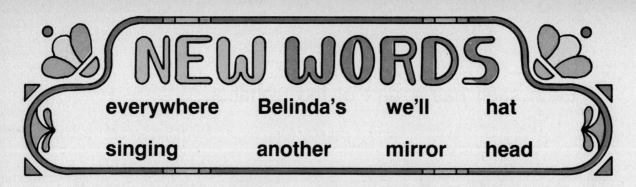

NEW WORDS

everywhere   Belinda's   we'll   hat

singing   another   mirror   head

These sentences are about "The New Spring Hats."
Circle each word that makes the sentence true.

1. In the spring flowers are _____.

here   there   down   (everywhere)

2. Birds are _____.

telling   helping   (singing)   liking

3. Belinda wanted a new _____.

mirror   (hat)   aunt   mitten

4. Her mother said, "_____ get you one."

I'm   Everyone   Ellen's   (We'll)

5. Belinda put a bowl on her _____.

room   stage   cat   (head)

6. Then she looked in a _____.

bowl   part   middle   (mirror)

7. She tried on _____ hat.

some   (another)   much   all

8. _____ hat was too big for her.

Belinda   Paint   Seeds   (Belinda's)

Level 8: "The New Spring Hats," Part One, pp. 108–114. (Vocabulary, Comprehension)
Objectives: To increase a basic reading vocabulary; to recall setting, characters, and events in a selection. **Directions:**
The children circle the word that makes the sentence true.

BLENDS

Circle the word that fits the picture.

hog
(frog)
flog

(tree)
bee
free

diver
over
(driver)

(play)
say
place

sock
clothes
(clock)

shower
(flower)
floor

crib
cab
(crab)

grew
(green)
seeds

brother
down
(brown)

sit
(sleep)
sheep

bird
house
(blue)

class
(glass)
grass

trick
duck
(truck)

(fly)
sky
flower

(prize)
breeze
size

Level 8: "The New Spring Hats," Part One, pp. 108–114. (Decoding/Encoding Skills)
Objective: To associate sounds and symbols for consonant blends (clusters) in the initial position: /br/br, /dr/dr, /fr/fr, /gr/gr, /kr/cr, /pr/pr, /tr/tr, /bl/bl, /fl/fl, /gl/gl, /kl/cl, /pl/pl, /sl/sl. **Directions:** Have the pictures identified. The children are to circle the word that matches the picture.

The Boy Roy

top

boat

oil

boy

Underline the letters that spell the vowel sound you hear in oil.

coin

toy

sock

coat

boil

note

Roy

hop

soap

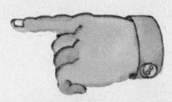

point

noise

soil

Level 8: "The New Spring Hats," Part One, pp. 108–114. (Decoding/Encoding Skills)
Objectives: To associate the vowel sounds and symbols: /ɔy/oi, oy as in *boy*. **Directions:** Have the pictures at the top identified and the short and long vowel sound spellings discussed. Then have the other pictures identified and the directions read. The children should be able to complete the page independently.

What Does It Mean?

Read each sentence.
Find the picture that goes with it.
Write the number of the picture in the box.

| 3 | She has a hat on her <u>head</u>. |

| 1 | Belinda is at the <u>head</u> of the line. |

| 2 | Daddy got a <u>head</u> of for our rabbit. |

| 2 | I will not <u>part</u> with my dog for a new dog. |

| 3 | Where do you <u>part</u> your hair? |

| 1 | The kangaroo had a good <u>part</u> in the play. |

Level 8: "The New Spring Hats," Part One, pp. 108–114. (Language Skills)
Objective: To identify the multiple meanings of given words. **Directions:** Have the children look at each row of pictures, discuss their content, and read the sentences under them. The children are then to write the number of the picture in the box next to the sentence that tells about it.

49

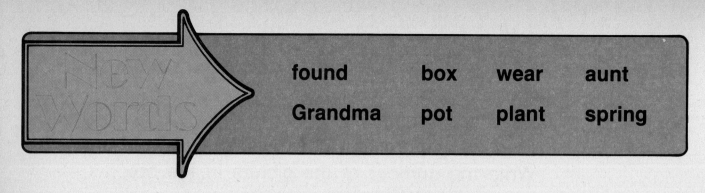
These sentences are about "The New Spring Hats."
Circle each word that makes the sentence true.

1. People like to get new hats in the _____ .

   bench   mirror   (spring)   park

2. Belinda wanted to _____ a new spring hat.

   come   pick   (wear)   eat

3. She went to her _____ with a new hat.

   (aunt)   Maggie   tryouts   squirrel

4. One of Belinda's hats was the cat's _____ .

   crab   (box)   elevator   button

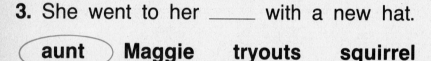

5. Belinda let _____ see her new spring hat.

   mirror   brother   Edward   (Grandma)

6. She tried to wear a _____ .

   chipmunk   birds   (pot)   spring

7. But then her father wanted it for a _____ .

   (plant)   bench   another   kangaroo

8. She looked in a box and _____ a new hat.

   (found)   did   called   wear

Level 8: "The New Spring Hats," Part Two, pp. 108–120. (Vocabulary, Comprehension)
Objectives: To increase a basic reading vocabulary; to recall setting, characters, and events in a selection. **Directions:**
The children circle the word that makes the sentence true.

50

Two Consonants With One Sound

Circle the word that fits the picture.

	sheep **(skirt)** sign		park pick **(mask)**
	(smell) sing small		**(chest)** let cherry
	sky **(spill)** sit		game crisp **(grasp)**
	sleep step **(stage)**		chest **(last)** let
	(skate) skin step		**(smash)** some smell
	small **(smoke)** sleep		save **(spoon)** spring

Level 8: "The New Spring Hats," Part Two, pp. 115–120. (Decoding/Encoding Skills)
Objective: To associate sounds for consonant blends (clusters) in the initial and final positions: /sm/sm, /sp/sp, /sk/sk, /st/st. **Directions:** Have the pictures identified. Then have the children circle the word that matches the picture.

51

Which Is the Question?

Draw a line under the question that goes with the answer.

Answer   **A puppy is in the box.**

Question   Where is the box?
When did the box come?
What is in the box?

Answer   **He is in back of the chair.**

Question   Where is he?
When will he come?
Who is he?

Answer   **Kim liked the blue bike.**

Question   Why did Kim like the bike?
Which bike did Kim like?
How much did Kim like it?

Level 8: ''The New Spring Hats,'' Part Two, pp. 115–120. (Language Skills)
Objective: To identify *who, what, when, where, why, which,* and *how* as words that often introduce questions. **Directions:** Have the children look at the pictures and read the questions. Then the children are to underline the question that goes with the answer.

52

NEW WORDS

| wish | Lassie | named | how |
| just | turtle | tweet | wag |

These sentences are about "All the Lassies."
Circle each word that makes the sentence true.

1. Peter said, "I _____ I had a dog."

   (wish)   come   find   could

2. He called his new goldfish _____.

   fire   part   (Lassie)   Mrs. Cook

3. But it didn't know _____ to come when he called.

   that   (how)   why   much

4. Next, his mother got him a _____.

   stage   (turtle)   kangaroo   mirror

5. Peter _____ the turtle "Lassie," too.

   thank   fit   turned   (named)

6. The turtle couldn't _____ its tail.

   (wag)   try   run   jump

7. Peter said, "I _____ wish I had a dog."

   away   (just)   much   one

8. All his next "Lassie" could say was "_____."

   Woof   (Tweet)   Moo   Meow

Level 8: "All the Lassies," Part One, pp. 124–128. (Vocabulary, Comprehension)
Objectives: To increase a basic reading vocabulary; to recall setting, characters, and events in a selection. **Directions:**
The children circle the word that makes the sentence true.

53

HER BIRTHDAY

Say these sentences.
Listen for the sound of the underlined letters.

We have a b<u>ir</u>d that says, "Happy B<u>ir</u>thday, G<u>ir</u>l."

She sits on a p<u>er</u>ch.

Underline the word that makes a sentence.

fern   skirt   <u>third</u>

The _____ girl has a red skirt.

clerk   <u>perch</u>   peach

The monkey is on a _____.

birth   <u>bird</u>   dirt

Here is a boy with a blue
shirt and a pet _____.

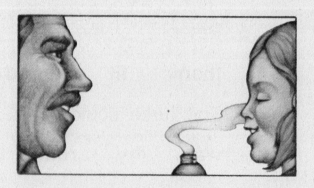

<u>perfume</u>   perch   shirt

The clerk let me smell
the _____.

Level 8: "All the Lassies," Part One, pp. 124–128. (Decoding/Encoding Skills)
Objective: To associate the vowel + r sounds and symbols /ər/ir, er as in bird and her. **Directions:** Have the children
read the sentence and listen for the sound of the underlined letters. Have the pictures identified. Then have the children
make a complete sentence by drawing a line under the missing word.

54

Which Is the Question?

Draw a line under the question that goes with the answer.

Answer   **Peter played all morning.**

Question   Why did Peter play?

             <u>When did Peter play?</u>

             How did Peter play?

Answer   **My cousin is in the car.**

Question   Where is the car?

             When did the cousin come?

             <u>Who is in the car?</u>

Answer   **Peter looks sick.**

Question   Why does Peter look sick?

             <u>How does Peter look?</u>

             When did Peter get sick?

Level 8: "All the Lassies," Part One, pp. 124–128. (Language Skills)
Objective: To identify question using *who, what, when,* and *where.* **Directions:** Have the children look at the pictures and read the questions. Then have the children underline the question that goes with the answer.

Circle the right word for each sentence.

1. "_____, I don't know where the cookies are."   **Know**   (**No**)

2. Do you _____ where the fire is?   (**know**)   **no**

3. My brother _____ the way to go.   (**knew**)   **new**

4. Do you want to play with my _____ game?   **knew**   (**new**)

5. I wish I _____ where the new park is.   (**knew**)   **new**

6. Sora saw someone she _____ at the new store.   (**knew**)   **new**

7. I can't say _____ to my friends.   **know**   (**no**)

8. Do you _____ about Belinda's hat?   (**know**)   **no**

9. I _____ where we can see a daddy longlegs.   (**know**)   **no**

10. I _____ that you would come.   (**knew**)   **new**

Level 8: "All the Lassies," Part One, pp. 124–128. (Language Skills)
Objective: To distinguish homophones: *no* and *know; new* and *knew.* **Directions:** Have the cartoon read. Then have children circle the right word for each sentence.

New Words

Walter	bring	ball
kittens	throw	
Lassies	just	

Write the missing word on the line.

1. Peter _____ wanted a dog.

just

2. I know someone who has two _____ .

kittens

3. One of the _____ was a kitten.

Lassies

4. "Go get the _____, Lassie!" said Peter.

ball

5. "You _____ it back to me," said Peter.

bring

6. "_____ is a good name for my dog," said Peter.

Walter

7. Peter would _____ the ball.

throw

8. Walter would _____ it back.

bring

Level 8: "All the Lassies," Part Two, pp. 129–133. (Vocabulary)
Objective: To increase a basic reading vocabulary. **Directions:** After the children have written the words on the lines, have them read the sentences aloud.

57

Belinda, Peter, and Walter

Fill in the circle by the sentence that tells about the picture.

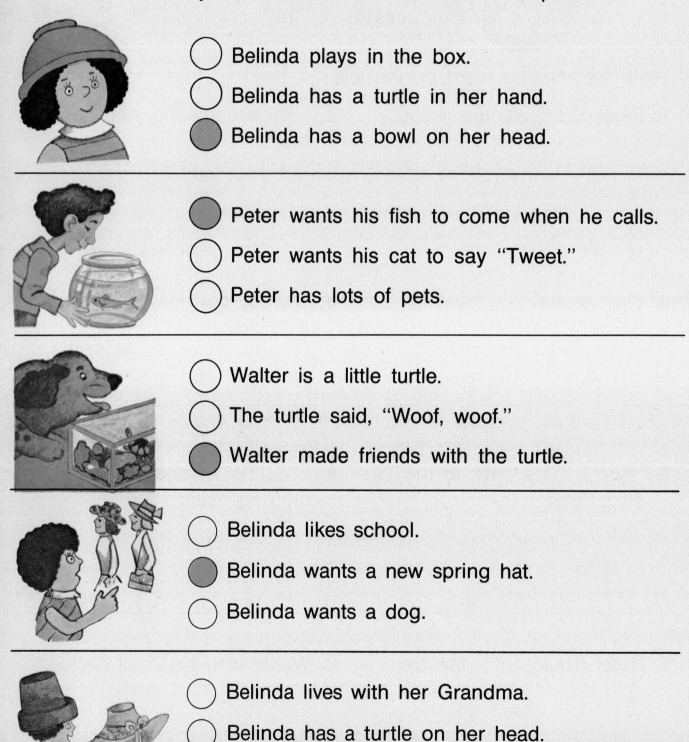

○ Belinda plays in the box.

○ Belinda has a turtle in her hand.

● Belinda has a bowl on her head.

● Peter wants his fish to come when he calls.

○ Peter wants his cat to say "Tweet."

○ Peter has lots of pets.

○ Walter is a little turtle.

○ The turtle said, "Woof, woof."

● Walter made friends with the turtle.

○ Belinda likes school.

● Belinda wants a new spring hat.

○ Belinda wants a dog.

○ Belinda lives with her Grandma.

○ Belinda has a turtle on her head.

● Belinda's father brings her a new spring hat.

Level 8: "All the Lassies," Part Two, pp. 124–133. (Comprehension)
Objective: To understand the direct, literal meaning of a sentence. **Directions:** Have the children fill in the circles by the sentences that best describe the pictures.

58

Words That End the Same

Say these words.
Listen for the sound the letters <u>ow</u> stand for.
grow   **throw**   **slow**   **snow**   **crow**

Write the missing <u>ow</u> word on the lines.

1. Throw the ball to me.

2. A crow is a big bird.

3. Juan plays in the snow.

4. Water helps flowers grow.

5. Turtles are very slow.

Level 8: "All the Lassies," Part Two, pp. 129–133. (Decoding/Encoding Skills)
Objective: To associate vowel sounds and symbols /ow/ow as in *show*. **Directions:** Say the words with the children.
Have the children write the missing word on the line.

59

One or Two Syllables?

Say these words.
Write the number of syllables you hear in each word.

dog ___1___ dishes ___2___ sisters ___2___

dogs ___1___ dish ___1___ sister ___2___

Circle the word that completes the sentence.

1. Some ____ are singing.

bird (birds)

2. Don't sit on that ____.

(bench) benches

3. Some ____ sleep all day.

cat (cats)

4. You may have three ____.

wish (wishes)

5. Mother put my toys into that ____.

(box) boxes

6. How many ____ were you sick?

day (days)

Level 8: "All the Lassies," Part Two, pp. 129–133. (Decoding)
Objective: To identify the number of syllables in a word when *s* or *es* is added to form a plural noun. **Directions:** Have children say each word and write the number of syllables they hear in each word. Then have children circle the word that completes each sentence.

Telling Where

Put an X before the words that tell **where.**

Jimmy ran

__X__ after the chipmunk.

_____ away from the chipmunk.

_____ fast.

The kitten jumped

_____ and looked.

__X__ on the box.

_____ quietly.

Sandy sat down

_____ and read.

_____ with a book.

__X__ on the floor.

They walked

_____ and talked.

_____ with the dog.

__X__ in the street.

Level 8: "All the Lassies," Part Two, pp. 129–133. (Language)
Objective: To use the prepositional phrases to tell where. **Directions:** Have children put an X before the phrase that tells where.

61

NEW WORDS

berries   cave   eating   near

winter   cold   climb   any

These sentences are about "Bert's Berries."
Circle the word that makes each sentence true.

1. All the other bears would sleep all _____.

window   day   morning   (winter)

2. But Bert sat in his _____ when they were sleeping.

(cave)   tree   apartment   box

3. Bert thought about _____.

Maggie   (berries)   room   kittens

4. In the winter it is too _____ for berries.

middle   up   (cold)   red

5. All night he thought about _____ berries.

jumping   throw   (eating)   called

6. He thought he would _____ a tree.

bring   (climb)   laugh   find

7. He went up and waited _____ the berries.

(near)   again   on   away

8. But he did not see _____ animal eat them.

every   all   (any)   two

Level 8: "Bert's Berries," Part One, pp. 134–137. (Vocabulary, Comprehension)
Objectives: To increase a basic reading vocabulary; to recall setting, characters, and events in a selection. **Directions:**
The children circle the word that makes the sentence true.

y as in happy

Say the words. Listen for the long e̲ sound.

| **puppy̲** | **city̲** | **lonely̲** |
| **any̲** | **every̲** | **daddy̲** |

Write the missing word on the line.

1. My _____ likes to pick berries.

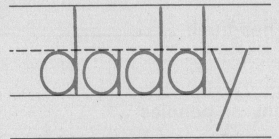

2. Sandy lives in the _____.

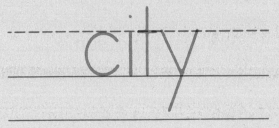

3. Did you get _____ sleep?

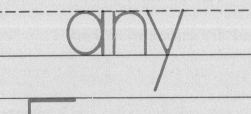

4. _____ flower is gone.

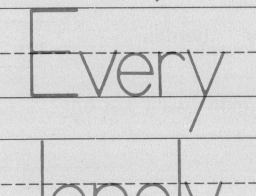

5. He looks very _____.

Level 8: ''Bert's Berries.'' Part One. pp. 134–137. (Decoding/Encoding Skills)
Objective: To associate vowel sounds and symbols: /iy/y as in *happy.* **Directions:** Have the children choose from the box a word that will make a sentence and write the word on the line.

63

MORE THAN ONE

Write the right word on the lines.

puppy   puppies

I have a little _puppy_ .

Jill has three _puppies_ .

penny   pennies

My mother gave me some _pennies_ .

Then I found one more _penny_ .

berry   berries

Bert didn't want just one _berry_ .

He wanted all the _berries_ .

Level 8: "Bert's Berries," Part One, pp. 138–144. (Language Skills)
Objective: To form plural nouns by changing *y* to *i* and adding the *-es* ending. **Directions:** Have the students write the correct word on the lines.

Making New Words with "Any"

This is a compound word. It is made up of two words.

any + one = anyone

Write the right word on the line.

1. You can put it ____.
   anywhere   anyone

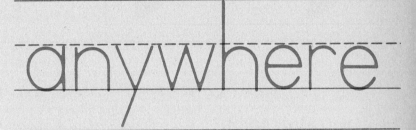

2. Did ____ find a ball?
   anytime   anyone

3. You may come____.
   anything   anytime

4. I don't want to eat ____.
   anything   anyone

5. Wouldn't ____ help you?
   anywhere   anyone

Level 8: "Bert's Berries," Part One, pp. 134–137. (Language Skills)
Objective: To construct compound words beginning with the word *any*. **Directions:** Have the children write the correct compound word on the line.

65

Words That Sound Alike

Circle the sentence that best tells about the picture.
Write the missing word in the last sentence.

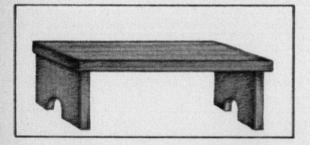

He **would** do that!

(The bench is made of **wood**.)

Put some  on the fire.

(I am **so** late!)

Please **sew** my pocket.

Your plants are big.

(They like to swim in the **sea**.)

They **see** the cave.

Can you take your boat out to  ?

Level 8: "Bert's Berries," Part One, pp. 134–137. (Language Skills)
Objective: To recognize and distinguish between homophones: *wood* and *would; so* and *sew; sea* and *see*. **Directions:** Have children read the directions. Have the children circle the sentence that matches the picture. Then have the children write in the missing word to make a sentence.

New Words

fox	because	other
why	began	eating
rabbits		

These sentences are about "Bert's Berries."
Circle the word that makes each sentence true.

1. Bert said, "Stop it!" when the ____ began to eat the berries.

bird (fox) kitten Lassie

2. He said "Stop, ____ I want them all.

and but then (because)

3. He did not want the fox or any ____ animal near them.

(other) new some old

4. The fox said, "____ do you want me to stop?"

Because Where (Why) Who

5. Bert was happy when the fox ____ to go.

went climb told (began)

6. ____ came to eat the berries.

Belinda's Tryouts (Rabbits) Turtles

7. Bert did not like to see them ____ the berries.

(eating) seeing jumping helping

Level 8: "Bert's Berries," Part Two, pp. 134–144. (Vocabulary, Comprehension)
Objectives: To increase a basic reading vocabulary; to recall setting, characters, and events in a selection. **Directions:** The children circle the word that makes the sentence true.

The Bear, the Rabbits, & the Fox

Write the number of the picture in front of the
words that tell about it.

3	could stop the rabbits from eating the berries.
1	liked lots of berries but no fish.
1	sat up in a tree.
3	just wanted to eat a little.
1	lived in a cave all winter.
2	didn't go when the bear asked them to go.
3	wanted to help Bert.
2	didn't care what the bear said.
1	was too big to run after the rabbits.
2	laughed at Bert.

Level 8: "Bert's Berries," Part Two, pp. 138–144. (Comprehension)
Objective: To recall details about the setting of a selection. **Directions:** Have the pictures identified. The children are
to write the number of the picture that corresponds to the phrase.

WHAT IS IT ABOUT?

Read about bears.

Bears eat berries.
But they eat other plants, too.
Some of the animals they eat are fish, frogs, and turtles.
When they can get big animals, they eat them, too.
Sometimes they eat birds.
Bears eat plants <u>and</u> animals.

Check the sentence that tells all about bears.

____Bert likes berries, fish, and frogs.
_✓_Bears eat lots of plants and animals.
____Bears eat birds if they can get them.
____Bears eat berries and other plants.

Read about Clarita.

Every spring Clarita helps her mother plant flowers.
They make a place for the flower seeds near the house.
Her mother puts the seeds down.
Clarita waters them.
When the flowers come up, Clarita is happy.

Check the sentence that tells all about Clarita.

____Clarita goes to the store with her mother.
____They make a place for the seeds by the house.
____Clarita is happy in the spring.
_✓_Every spring Clarita helps her mother plant flowers.

Level 8: ''Bert's Berries,'' Part Two, pp. 134–137. (Comprehension)
Objective: To explain and evaluate the theme of a story. **Directions:** The children check the sentence that expresses the main idea of the paragraph.

Double Consonant Letters

Say the word for each picture.
Circle the missing letters.

sa _ _ le

ll   ss   (dd)

do _ _ ar

(ll)   ss   dd

dru _ _ er

(mm)   ss   tt

ru _ _ er

tt   (nn)   ss

a _ _ le

rr   ll   (pp)

che _ _ y

(rr)   ll   pp

bu _ _ on

mm   rr   (tt)

ta _ _ el

mm   rr   (ss)

le _ _ er

(tt)   nn   ss

Level 8: "Bert's Berries," Part Two, pp. 134–144. (Phonology)
Objectives: To associate consonant phonemes and graphemes in the medial position: /d/*dd*, /l/*ll*, /m/*mm*, /n/*nn*, /p/*pp*, /r/*rr*, /s/*ss*, /t/*tt*; to identify vowel letters as standing for short vowel sounds when they are followed by double consonant letters. **Directions:** A. The children circle the double consonant letters. They underline the preceding vowel letters. B. The children are to make the generalization that a vowel letter before double consonant letters stands for a short vowel sound.

70

How Many Do You Know?

Circle the word your teacher reads.

ones	(wish)	birds	jumping
other	we'll	(because)	jump
(own)	wag	box	(just)
over	wear	being	jumps
how	(middle)	rabbits	away
helped	mirror	run	(another)
hats	mitten	(room)	any
(head)	much	raccoon	aunt
care	know	sky	(began)
(clothes)	kite	spring	ball
cave	(kangaroo)	singing	bring
called	kittens	(stage)	berries
noon	tweet	(why)	eating
named	tryouts	winter	everywhere
(near)	turtle	Walter	(everyone)
next	(throw)	where	every

Level 8: "Bert's Berries," Part Two, pp. 138–144. (Vocabulary)
Objective: To increase a basic reading vocabulary. **Directions:** Pronounce the word circled in the Teacher's Edition.
Use the word in a sentence and then pronounce it again. The children are to circle the word in their books. For an
optional extended test, pronounce each underlined word. The circled and underlined words are high frequency words.

NEW WORDS

family	only	somewhere	think
Sundays	zoo	anywhere	tigers

These sentences are about "A Place for Carmen."
Circle the word that makes each sentence true.

1. Everyone but Carmen went _____.

   (somewhere) **sometimes** **there** **here**

2. Carmen's sister and brother were part of her _____.

   fox **Grandma** **(family)** **floor**

3. Grandma went to the country on _____.

   tigers **stores** **someone** **(Sundays)**

4. Carmen thought she was the _____ one who never went places.

   lonely **(only)** **new** **good**

5. She said, "I never go _____."

   very **there** **here** **(anywhere)**

6. Carmen had to _____ about where to go.

   climb **forget** **(think)** **began**

7. Pablo wanted to see kangaroos and _____.

   berries **kittens** **trucks** **(tigers)**

8. Carmen said, "We will go to the _____."

   Sunday **(zoo)** **lot** **driver**

Level 8: "A Place for Carmen," pp. 158–169. (Vocabulary, Comprehension)
Objectives: To increase a basic reading vocabulary; to recall setting, characters, and events in a selection. **Directions:**
The children circle the word that makes the sentence true.

er **ur** **ir**

h<u>er</u>   f<u>ur</u>   b<u>ir</u>d

Circle the word that makes a sentence.

1. I like the smell of this ____.

fan   perch   (perfume)

2. A ____ is growing next to the flowers.

fan   (fern)   perfume

3. I can't find my ____.

sky   (purse)   hurts

4. A ____ looks like a bird.

nurse   purse   (turkey)

5. A ____ takes care of sick people.

(nurse)   purse   turkey

6. This blue ____ does not sing.

skirt   (bird)   pail

7. My new ____ is red.

(skirt)   bird   pail

Level 8: "A Place for Carmen," pp. 158–169. (Decoding/Encoding Skills)
Objective: To associate vowel + r sounds and symbols /ər/er, ir, ur as in her, bird, and nurse. **Directions:** Have the children read the words at the top of the page and determine that the underlined letters stand for the same sound. Have the pictures identified and the words read. Then have the children circle the word that makes a sentence.

73

Who Said That ?

On the lines, write who is talking.

Grandma   **Pablo**   **Carmen**   **Rosa**

Mother   **Daddy**

"I'm the only one who never goes places. Why is that?" asked _____.

Carmen .

"Maybe you could if you asked about it," said _____.

Grandma.

"Where do you want to go?" asked _____.

Mother .

"Read me a story," said _____.

Pablo .

"Sunday is coming, Carmen. Have you thought about where you want to go?" asked _____.

Daddy .

Level 8: "A Place for Carmen," pp. 158–169. (Language Skills)
Objectives: To recognize the purpose of quotation marks; to recall details about characters. **Directions:** Have the directions and names read. Have the children write the name of the speaker on the lines.

WHAT IS IT ABOUT?

Read about Teddy and Don.

Teddy has a brother named Don.
Don and Teddy have a dog named Lassie and a cat named Tim.
The cat and dog are good friends.
Don asked their mother if they could have a bird.
Their mother said, "No. What if Tim got the bird?
You and Don are in school all day.
You could not take care of the bird."
So the boys still have a dog and cat.
But they don't have a bird.

Write an answer to each question.

1. What is the name of the dog?

2. Who asked their mother for a bird?

3. What is the name of the cat?

4. Do Don and Teddy have a bird?

Level 8: "A Place for Carmen," pp. 158–169. (Comprehension)
Objective: To skim a selection in order to locate specific information. **Directions:** The children write answers to the questions after skimming the paragraph.

First Next Last

What happened first? Next? Last?
Write **1, 2,** or **3** in the boxes.

1

3

2

---

2 Amy reached the button.

1 Amy got in the elevator.

3 The elevator went up.

2 Don climbed up the tree.

3 Don picked the apples.

1 Don saw the apples.

---

3 Flowers never grow.

1 Mother plants the seeds.

2 Birds eat the seeds.

3 Mother tried on the hat.

2 Mother saw a hat.

1 Mother opened the box.

Level 8: "The Browns Say Good-by," Part One. pp. 171–177. (Comprehension)
Objective: To arrange events in sequence. **Directions:** Have the children number the pictures and sentences to show order of events.

"ar" RIDDLES

Circle the word that answers the riddle.

1. People sit in it to go from one place to another.

book (car)
yard tree

---

2. Plants grow in it and people play games in it.

star sky
leg (park)

---

3. It is not the end.

cart wolf
(start) box

---

4. You have one in a play.

lard (part)
truck pot

---

5. You see cows, sheep, and plants there.

shark button
bird (farm)

---

6. Cows moo and dogs _____ .

open (bark)
dart ask

Level 8: "The Browns Say Good-by," Part One, pp. 171–177. (Decoding/Encoding Skills)
Objective: To associate sounds and symbols: /ar/ar as in car. **Directions:** Read the words on the right with the children. Then have the children circle the word that answers the riddle.

77

NEW WORDS

moving	gave	bedroom	soon
putting	tonight	same	last

These sentences are about "The Browns Say Good-by."
Circle the word that makes each sentence true.

1. The Browns were _____ to a new town.

(moving)   putting   helping   jumping

2. Mrs. Brown was _____ clothes in boxes.

liking   going   (putting)   playing

3. Bobby _____ away his pets.

aren't   (gave)   said   gone

4. The new house was not the _____ as the old one.

bad   good   small   (same)

5. But Bobby said, "I'll stay here _____."

toy   (tonight)   morning   night

6. He said his pets would like his _____.

bench   kite   (bedroom)   men

7. Very _____ Bobby liked the new tree.

when   off   again   (soon)

8. At _____ Bobby was happy in his new house.

blue   just   (last)   own

Level 8: "The Browns Say Good-by," Part Two, pp. 171–185. (Vocabulary, Comprehension)
Objectives: To increase a basic reading vocabulary; to recall setting, characters, and events in a selection. **Directions:** The children circle the word that makes the sentence true.

BLENDS

Say these words. Listen to the sound of the underlined letters.

scream **spring** **three** **squirrel** **street**

Circle the sentence that best tells about the picture.

That's a very strong bench.

We want to put string in this box.

Bobby has three boxes for us.

Have you found the string yet?

We are going somewhere special.

She spread the seeds for the birds.

The brown thread is for his brown clothes.

Are these your spring clothes?

I thought she would do a trick.

Sandy lives on this street.

We want some yellow thread.

Did that squirrel throw a nut at me?

Level 8: "The Browns Say Good-by," Part Two, pp. 178–185. (Decoding/Encoding Skills)
Objectives: To associate consonant sounds and symbols for blends (clusters): /skr/scr, /skw/squ, /spr/spr, /str/str, /θr/thr. **Directions:** Have the children say the words and listen for the sound of the first three letters. Have the children circle the sentence that best tells about the picture.

"or" RIDDLES

Say these words. Listen for the <u>or</u> sound.
p<u>or</u>ch   w<u>or</u>n   sh<u>or</u>t   st<u>or</u>m   f<u>or</u>

Circle the word that answers the riddle.

1. You eat with it.

  from   for
  shore   (fork)

2. People lived here.

  fat   frog
  moving   (fort)

3. Something to eat.

  car   soon
  (corn)   cork

4. Another word for small.

  park   sport
  same   (short)

5. The first part of the day.

  north   street
  (morning)   putting

6. Another word for games.

  (sport)   speak
  tonight   porch

7. A word that may tell where to go.

  short   corn
  story   (north)

Level 8: "Our Trip," Part One, pp. 188–193. (Decoding/Encoding Skills)
Objective: To associate vowel + *r* sounds and symbols: /ɔr/*or* as in *for*. **Directions:** Have the children read the words on the right. Have them read the riddle and circle the word that answers the riddle.

The Consonant Sounds of g

Listen to the sound of g in giant and page.
Circle the pictures that have the same sound.

| cage | stage | rug | giraffe |

| frog | page | magic | gate |

Listen to the sound of g in dog and girl.
Circle the pictures that have the same sound.

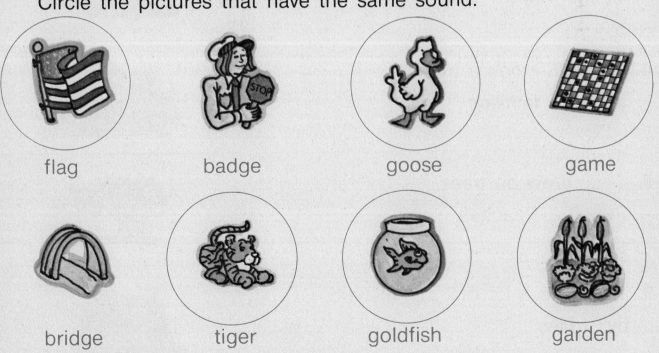

| flag | badge | goose | game |

| bridge | tiger | goldfish | garden |

Level 8: "Our Trip," Part One, pp. 188–193. (Decoding/Encoding Skills)
Objective: To associate vowel sounds and symbols /j/g as in *giant* and *page;* /g/g as in *dog* and *girl.* **Directions:**
In Part One, the children circle the pictures whose names have the same sound as the g in *giant* and *page.* In the
second part, they circle the pictures whose names have the same sound as the g in *dog* and *girl.*

More Than One

hat	bench	puppy
hats	benches	puppies

Circle the word that makes a sentence.

1. We have six _____ in our house.
room ⟨rooms⟩

2. Our class has all the _____.
ball ⟨balls⟩

3. This book is about a _____.
⟨fox⟩ foxes

4. Our _____ took a trip.
⟨family⟩ families

5. _____ grow on trees.
Peach ⟨Peaches⟩

6. There are a lot of _____ in here.
fly ⟨flies⟩

Level 8: "Our Trip," Part One, pp. 188–193. (Language Skills)
Objective: To form plurals by adding *s* or *es* and by changing *y* to *i* before adding *es*. **Directions:** Have children circle the word that completes each sentence.

NEW WORDS

beautiful   cherry   lights   hand

anything   state   best   stood

These sentences are about "Our Trip."
Circle the word that makes each sentence true.

1. Jimmy said, "You don't know _____."

    it   any   our   (anything)

2. There is a city of Washington and a _____ of Washington.

    room   (state)   Sunday   store

3. The _____ trees had pink flowers on them.

    trip   room   (cherry)   Chang

4. Washington Monument is very _____.

    (beautiful)   blue   pink   happy

5. Jimmy said the Monument was the _____ part of the trip.

    last   bad   most   (best)

6. At night there are _____ on the Monument.

    lots   (lights)   legs   flowers

7. The girl held her father's _____.

    (hand)   motel   hat   state

8. They _____ looking at the Monument.

    (stood)   sleep   shower   wanted

Level 8: "Our Trip," Part Two, pp. 188–200. (Vocabulary, Comprehension)
Objectives: To increase a basic reading vocabulary; to recall setting, characters, and events in a selection. Directions:
The children circle the word that makes the sentence true.

83

The Consonant Sounds of c

Listen to the sound of <u>c</u> in <u>c</u>ity and pla<u>c</u>e.
Circle the pictures that have the same sound.

face	cup	mice	ceiling
ice	attic	race	cake

Listen to the sound of <u>c</u> in <u>c</u>old and be<u>c</u>ause.
Circle the pictures that have the same sound.

cave	picnic	cupcake	city
dance	can	raccoon	pencil

Level 8: "Our Trip," Part Two, pp. 188–200. (Decoding Encoding Skills)
Objective: To associate consonant sounds and symbols in the initial, medial, and final positions: /k/c and /s/c. **Directions:** Have the children circle the pictures whose name contains /s/. Have the children circle the pictures whose name contains /k/.

What Is It About?

Read about Bobby.

On Sunday Bobby went on a car trip with his father.
When it was time to go, his mother gave him some
cherries to eat.
Bobby liked to look out the car window at people.
He saw the most people in the city.
After that, Bobby saw green trees and beautiful cows.
There was a frog in the road.
His father stopped so Bobby could see it.
It was dark when they got home.
His mother stood at the door waiting for them.

Write an answer for each question. Use one or two words.

1. When did Bobby and his father go in the car?

Sunday

2. What beautiful animals did Bobby see?

cows

3. When did they get home?

at dark

4. Who stood waiting for them?

his mother

Level 8: "Our Trip," Part Two, pp. 188–198. (Comprehension)
Objective: To skim a selection in order to locate specific information. **Directions:** The children answer the questions after skimming the paragraph.

85

NEW WORDS

walking   heard   bite   camel

everything   been   eyes   nut

These sentences are about "The Camel Who Went for a Walk." Circle the word that makes each sentence true.

1. _____ in the forest was quiet.

It   **(Everything)**   Us   Another

2. The tiger had _____ sleeping.

do   be   was   **(been)**

3. The tiger _____ the camel.

(heard)   jumped   helped   forgot

4. The camel had beautiful _____.

tails   **(eyes)**   trees   roads

5. The monkey reached for a _____.

flower   tree   tiger   **(nut)**

6. The squirrel did not _____ the monkey's tail.

walking   began   **(bite)**   like

7. The animals thought the _____ would walk by the tree.

tiger   bird   **(camel)**   cow

8. But then the camel was _____ away.

waiting   reached   tried   **(walking)**

Level 8: "The Camel Who Went for a Walk," pp. 202–214. (Vocabulary, Comprehension)
Objectives: To increase a basic reading vocabulary; to recall setting, characters, and events in a selection. **Directions:** The children circle the word that makes a true sentence about the story.

SYLLABLES

Circle the number of syllables in the underlined words.

1. Who <u>came</u> in the door?   ① 2 3

2. That's a nice brown <u>camel</u>.   1 ② 3

3. Is that book <u>for</u> me?   ① 2 3

4. Lots of trees are in the <u>forest</u>.   1 ② 3

5. We were in <u>every</u> room.   1 ② 3

6. We will see you this <u>afternoon</u>.   1 2 ③

7. May we have <u>some</u> water?   ① 2 3

8. There's <u>something</u> in this water.   1 ② 3

9. What can that <u>be</u>?   ① 2 3

10. Have you <u>been</u> here long?   ① 2 3

11. They went for a <u>walk</u> in the park.   ① 2 3

12. She is <u>walking</u> up and down the road.   1 ② 3

13. The mouse <u>bit</u> the dog.   ① 2 3

14. I can't wait to <u>bite</u> into a cookie.   ① 2 3

15. Have you <u>any</u> boxes?   1 ② 3

16. You can put <u>anything</u> in this big box.   1 2 ③

17. Something is in my <u>eye</u>.   ① 2 3

18. Your <u>eyes</u> are beautiful.   ① 2 3

Level 8: ''The Camel Who Went for a Walk,'' pp. 202–214. (Decoding/Encoding Skills)
Objective: To identify the number of syllables up to three in a word. **Directions:** The children are to read each sentence and then circle the number of syllables in the underlined word.

87

ABCDE   FGHIJ   KLMNO   PQRSTU   VWXYZ

Write the words in alphabetical order.

camel been eyes frog dark | **nut lights knows over made**

1. been

2. camel

3. dark

4. eyes

5. frog

1. knows

2. lights

3. made

4. nut

5. over

Level 8: ''The Camel Who Went for a Walk,'' pp. 202–214. (Study Skills)
Objective: To arrange words in alphabetical order. **Directions:** Have the letters on the tapes at the top of the page read. Have the words read and then written in alphabetical order.

NEW WORDS

wherever   I've   page   way

whirl   rook   hole   log

These sentences are about "Where Have You Been?"
Circle the word that makes each sentence true.

1. "That's where _____ been," said the cat.

I'm   (I've)   We'll   I'll

2. The squirrel knows how to _____.

got   will   (whirl)   read

3. The fish swims _____ it wants.

(wherever)   but   why   that

4. Do you know the _____ up the road?

day   earmuffs   wings   (way)

5. When a tree is down it's a _____.

frog   mole   (log)   leg

6. Was anything in the _____ with the mole?

toad   (hole)   clock   hand

7. One bird in the story was the _____.

book   bunny   (rook)   raccoon

8. On what _____ of the book was the rook?

park   room   log   (page)

Level 8: "Where Have You Been?" pp. 216–229. (Vocabulary, Comprehension)
Objectives: To increase a basic reading vocabulary; to recall setting, characters, and events in a selection. **Directions:**
The children circle the word that makes the sentence true.

Where Have You Been?

These sentences are about "Where Have You Been?"
Each sentence tells where one animal was.
Write the name of the animal after each sentence.

frog   fish   toad   mouse   bunny   mole

1. I've been way up the road. _toad_

2. I've been sitting on a log. _frog_

3. I swim wherever I wish. _fish_

4. I've been running for fun. _bunny_

5. I've been in a hole. _mole_

6. I've been in a clock. _mouse_

Level 8: "Where Have You Been?" pp. 216–229. (Vocabulary, Comprehension)
Objectives: To increase a basic reading vocabulary; to recall setting, characters, and events in a selection. **Directions:** The children write the name of the animal before the words used by the animal in the poem.

Short Vowels

Say these words. Listen to the vowel sound you hear.

h<u>a</u>t   p<u>i</u>g   b<u>e</u>d   h<u>o</u>t   c<u>u</u>p

Circle the sentence that best tells about the picture.

The dog wigs his tail.

(The dog wags his tail.)

The dog wages his tail.

Your thimble is part of your hand.

(Your thumb is part of your hand.)

Your three is part of your hand.

Do you sleep in that bid?

(Do you sleep in that bed?)

Do you sleep in that bud?

The clash goes tack-tock.

The click goes tuck-tock.

(The clock goes tick-tock.)

Level 8: ''Where Have You Been?'' pp. 216–229. (Decoding/Encoding Skills)
Objective: To associate vowel sounds and symbols /æ/a as in cat, /e/e as in bed, /i/i as in pig, /a/o as in sock, /ə/u as in cup. **Directions:** Have the children say the words and listen for the short vowel sound. Then have them read the sentences and circle the sentence that best describes the picture.

BLENDS

Circle the word that makes a sentence.

1. Their cow is _____ and white.   crown   (brown)

2. Will that plant _____ big?   (grow)   crow

3. Can your dog do a _____?   (trick)   brick

4. Do you know how far a _____ jumps?   drop   (frog)

---

5. Who was the _____ of that car?   brother   (driver)

6. How do you cook a _____?   (crab)   grab

7. They gave a _____ to the best dog.   freeze   (prize)

8. I'll put a bench by the _____.   green   (tree)

---

9. The best way to cook this is to _____ it.   dry   (fry)

10. Tigers _____ water from this hole.   grin   (drink)

11. I will _____ to climb this tree.   (try)   fry

12. We went on a long _____.   drip   (trip)

Level 8: "Where Have You Been?" pp. 216–229. (Decoding/Encoding Skills)
Objective: To associate consonant sounds and symbols for blends (clusters) in the initial position: /br/br, /dr/dr, /fr/fr, /gr/gr, /kr/cr, /pr/pr, /tr/tr. **Directions:** Have the children read the sentence and circle the word that completes the sentence.

Following Directions

Make a tree for the squirrel to sit in.
Put some nuts in the hole.
Give the boy a kite.

Children's Art

Put a box in the back of the truck.
Put a tire on the car.
Make a road for the car and truck.

Children's Art

Give the raccoon an apple.
Give the kitten a ball.
Put the goldfish in a bowl.

Children's Art

Level 8: ''Where Have You Been?'' pp. 216–229. (Study Skills)
Objective: To follow written directions. **Directions:** Have children read the sentences and do what they are asked to do.

93

How Many Do You Know?

Circle the word your teacher reads.

would	bite	our	(something)
wherever	(best)	off	somewhere
(way)	been	oh	same
whirl	beautiful	(only)	soon
tick	red	head	nut
(think)	rabbits	(heard)	near
tonight	run	how	(never)
took	(real)	hand	next
(any)	cold	(over)	plant
another	clothes	opened	paint
aunt	(called)	other	pot
away	cave	own	(part)
this	smells	alone	(has)
their	(school)	asks	help
telling	sometimes	(after)	her
(take)	still	about	he's

Level 8: "Where Have You Been?" pp. 216–229. (Vocabulary)
Objective: To increase a basic reading vocabulary. **Directions:** Pronounce the word circled in the Teacher's Edition. Use the word in a sentence and then pronounce it again. The children are to circle the word in their books. For an optional extended test, pronounce each underlined word. The circled and underlined words are high frequency words.

94

Dear Parent,

Your child has just completed the first unit in a reader entitled *A Time for Friends*. In this unit, your child read nine selections and was taught 78 new vocabulary words. The theme of this book is friends and friendship. The first unit, called "All Kinds of Friends," included a story about the friendship of two girls who live in an apartment house, a story about a friendship between two boys that is threatened when one of the boys makes a new friend, and a story about an elephant with an injured leg, who asks all his friends for advice. In a career awareness section, your child read about neighborhood friends, such as police officers, who perform community services.

The phonics skills taught in this unit included the common spelling patterns for the long vowel sounds, such as *ai* in *tail* for the long *a* sound, *ee* in *feet* for the long *e* sound, and *o-e* in *home* for the long *o* vowel sound. Your child also studied synonyms (words with similar meanings) and the construction of both simple declarative sentences and "yes–no" questions. Building a basic reading vocabulary and understanding meaning in paragraphs and sentences were also emphasized.

As a parent, you can do a great deal to help your child become a better reader. Taking your child to the library regularly and reading aloud daily will help build a love of books and reading. You can also reinforce what your child is learning at school by working with the vocabulary words, story, and game on these pages.

Answers to questions on page 98: 1. *an apartment;* 2. *Mr. Greenthumb;* 3. *cookies;* 4. *paint;* 5. *Mr. Greenthumb.*

Here are two home activities that will help reinforce phonics work done at school.

1. Print the word pairs below on a sheet of paper (but do not underline any letters.) Read the two words in each pair, and have your child tell you whether the vowel sound in each word is short or long. (Answers are in parentheses.) Then ask your child to read each word and have her or him draw a line under the letter or letters in each word that stand for the vowel sound. (The correct letters have been underlined here.)

red (short)	meet (long)	dim (short)	hope (long)
read (long)	met (short)	dime (long)	hop (**short**)
pail (long)	cut (short)	goat (long)	cape (long)
pal (short)	cute (long)	got (short)	cap (short)

2. Print the following letters and bases, each on a separate card:

Letters

r, s, t, p

Bases

ing, ack, an, eam

Give your child the letter cards and ask him or her to make words by putting each letter, in turn, at the beginning of each base. Possible words are: *ring, rack, ran, ream, sing, sack, seam, tack, tan, team.*

Sincerely,

_____

Your child was introduced to the words below in Unit 1 of *A Time for Friends*. You may wish to print each word on individual 3" × 5" pieces of paper, oaktag, or index cards. When your child can read quickly each of the words, try putting several words together to form a phrase or sentence, for example, "Rosa's buttons" or "Mr. Greenthumb waited for the doctor."

about	floor	leg	smells
after	fly	legs	sometimes
alone	forget	liking	still
apartment	forgot	lives	
apples			take
asks	green	Mr. Greenthumb	talk
	grew	Mr. Greenthumb's	telling
bad	grow		thank
brothers		next	thanks
button	help	nights	that's
buttons	helping		their
	her	opened	this
cousin	he's		thumb
cousin's		paint	tried
crab	isn't	picked	try
daddy-longlegs	Jimmy	reach	wait
doctor	Jimmy's	red	waited
	jump	Rosa	waiting
Edward		Rosa's	walk
Edward's	Kim		walked
elevator	Kim's	sat	wants
every		school	without
		seeds	worked
		smell	would

Note to parent: The following two pages include a story with some of the new words introduced in the first unit of *A Time for Friends* and a comprehension exercise similar to those done in the classroom. Your child may wish to read the story either silently or out loud.

HOLT BASIC READING, Workbook, *A Time for Friends*, Unit 1
Parent Component   Holt, Rinehart and Winston, Publishers

Rosa Finds a Friend

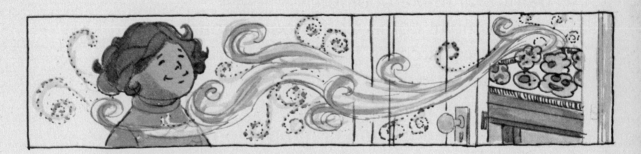

Rosa lived in an apartment.
Mr. Greenthumb lived next door.
Many smells came from Mr. Greenthumb's
apartment.

One morning Rosa was lonely.
"I smell a good smell," she said.
"It smells like cookies.
Can we make cookies? " Rosa asked.
Rosa and Mother made cookies.
She forgot she was lonely.

One afternoon Rosa was lonely.
"I smell paint," she said.
"I smell a paint smell from next door.
I will paint a picture."
Rosa did. And she forgot she was lonely.

Mr. Greenthumb was lonely, too.
One morning he came to Rosa's apartment.
Rosa's mother let him in.
And Rosa found a friend!

Now Rosa and Mr. Greenthumb
paint and make cookies.
Good smells come from Rosa's apartment.
Good smells come from Mr. Greenthumb's
apartment.
Rosa is not lonely now.
And Mr. Greenthumb is happy, too!

Note to parent: After your child has read the story, have him or her read each sentence below and circle the word or words that correctly completes the sentence according to the story. Answers are on page 95.

---

1. Rosa lived in _____.

   an elevator   an apartment   a carnival

2. Next door to Rosa lived _____.
   Kim   Mr. Greenthumb   Edward

3. Rosa and her mother made _____.
   paint   crab   cookies

4. One afternoon a _____ smell came from next door.
   country   paint   city

5. Rosa's new friend was _____.
   Mr. Greenthumb   Mother   Clarita

HOLT BASIC READING, Workbook, *A Time for Friends,* Unit 1
Parent Component   Holt, Rinehart and Winston, Publishers

Blend Concentration

brown	Brad
green	grow
stop	store
frog	friend
trees	tried

Note to Parent: This game will help reinforce the consonant blends *br*, *gr*, *st*, *fr*, and *tr*. Help your child cut out the ten word cards. Mix up the cards and place them in two rows, word side down. The first player chooses two cards and reads each word. If the two words begin with the same blend, the player keeps the cards. If not, he or she replaces the cards, and the next player takes a turn. The game continues until there are no cards left.

Dear Parent,

Your child has just completed the second unit in a reader entitled *A Time for Friends*. In this unit, your child read nine selections and was taught 78 new vocabulary words. This second unit, called "All Kinds of Families," included a story about a middle child's struggle to find her identity, and a story about a bear who discovers that only by sharing his berry patch with a fox can he save the entire patch from being devoured by rabbits. In the career awareness section of this unit, your child read about workers who perform services for various families, and a special fine arts section, called "The Family in Art," contained reproductions of well-known paintings of families.

The phonics skills taught in this unit included identifying the *y* spelling for the long *e* vowel sound heard at the end of *happy,* the *ow* spelling for the long *o* vowel sound heard in *low,* and the vowel sounds represented by the *oi, oy, ou,* and *ow* spellings. Your child also learned to identify compound words, to put words in alphabetical order, and to construct questions beginning with *who, what, when, where,* and *why.* Continued emphasis was given to building a basic reading vocabulary and to understanding meaning in paragraphs and stories.

As a parent, you can do a great deal to help your child become a better reader. Taking your child to the library regularly and reading aloud daily will help build a love of books and reading. You can also reinforce what your child is learning at school by working with the vocabulary words and other activities on these pages.

Here are some home activities that will reinforce phonics work done at school.

1. Provide your child with pencil and paper. Then say each of the words listed below, one at a time. Ask your child to listen carefully to the consonant sound in the middle of each word. Then have her or him write the consonant letter that stands for the middle sound. (Answers are underlined here.)

wa<u>g</u>on   mo<u>n</u>ey   wo<u>m</u>an   do<u>z</u>en   pa<u>r</u>ent   sai<u>l</u>or   la<u>b</u>el   wa<u>t</u>er

2. Then say each of the words below, one at a time. This time, ask your child to listen for the middle consonant sound and to write the <u>two</u> letters that stand for the sound she or he hears. (Answers are underlined.)

la<u>dd</u>er   pu<u>zz</u>le   zi<u>pp</u>er   mu<u>ff</u>in   le<u>ss</u>on   ra<u>bb</u>it   wi<u>gg</u>le   co<u>ll</u>ar

Sincerely,

_____

Teacher

Answers to exercises on page 104: The correct order for the sentences is 5, 3, 1, 4, 2.

Note to Parent: Your child was introduced to the words below in Unit 2 of *A Time for Friends*. For home practice, you may wish to print each word on individual 3" × 5" pieces of paper, oaktag, or index cards. When your child can read quickly each of the words, try putting several words together to form a phrase, sentence or question, for example, "Ellen's own room" or "Mrs. Cook called Belinda's aunt."

another	eating	kangaroo	part
any	Ellen	kittens	plant
aunt	Ellen's		pot
away	everyone	Lassie	
	everywhere	Lassies	rabbits
ball			room
because	fit	Maggie	run
began	found	Maggie's	
being	fox	middle	singing
Belinda		Mike	spring
Belinda's	Grandma	mirror	stage
berries		Mrs. Chang	
Bert	hat	Mrs. Chang's	throw
Bert's	hats	Mrs. Cook	tryouts
birds	head		turtle
box	helped	named	tweet
bring	how	near	
		noon	wag
called	jumping		Walter
care	jumps	ones	wear
cave	just	other	we'll
climb		over	why
cothes		own	winter
cold			wish

Note to parent: The following two pages include a story with some of the new words introduced in the second unit of *A Time for Friends* and a comprehension exercise similar to those done in the classroom. Your child may wish to read the story either silently or out loud.

HOLT BASIC READING, Workbook, *A Time for Friends*, Unit 2
Parent Component   Holt, Rinehart and Winston, Publishers

A Doctor Helps

Mrs. Chang had a kangaroo.
But her kangaroo would <u>not</u> jump.
Everyone tried to make the kangaroo jump.
The kangaroo would not.

Mrs. Chang said, "This kangaroo needs a
doctor."
She took the kangaroo to town.
In town, she found an animal doctor.

The kangaroo sat still in the waiting room.
Soon the doctor called Mrs. Chang.
Mrs. Chang and the kangaroo went in.

"My kangaroo will sit," said Mrs. Chang.
"My kangaroo will play.
This kangaroo will eat and sleep.
But my kangaroo will <u>not</u> jump."

The doctor got out some berries.
He put them up on a big box.
The kangaroo could smell the berries.
But he could not reach them.

Up jumped the kangaroo.
He jumped and jumped.
"Berries!" said Mrs. Chang.
"My kangaroo will jump for berries!
Thank you for helping, Doctor."
And Mrs. Chang took her jumping kangaroo
home.

Note to parent: After your child has read the story, have him/her number the sentences below to show the order in which they happened. The first one has already been done. Answers are on page 101.

| | Mrs. Chang took her kangaroo home. |

| | The doctor put berries on a box. |

| 1 | Mrs. Chang took the kangaroo to town. |

| | The kangaroo jumped to get the berries. |

| | The kangaroo sat in the waiting room. |

HOLT BASIC READING, Workbook, *A Time for Friends*, Unit 2
Parent Component   Holt, Rinehart and Winston, Publishers

Dear Parent,

Your child has just completed the third and final unit in a reader entitled *A Time for Friends*. In this unit, your child read six selections and was taught 111 new words. Many of the new words reflect the phonics skills that were taught in the unit. These skills include identifying vowel sounds for words with *vowel + r* spellings such as *car* and *for,* and a review of short and long vowel sounds. Continued emphasis was given to expanding reading vocabulary, understanding paragraph and story content, and identifying main ideas.

The third unit of *A Time for Friends* is called "Places to Go." In it, your child read a story about a boy who moves to a new home, a selection about a family's trip to Washington, D.C., and a fable entitled "The Camel Who Went for a Walk." In the career awareness section of this unit, your child read about the jobs of various transportation workers.

As a parent, you can do a great deal to help your child become a better reader. Taking your child to the library regularly and reading aloud daily will help build a love of books and reading. You can reinforce what your child is learning at school by working with the activities on these pages.

Here are some activities that will reinforce phonics work done at school.

1. Provide your child with pencil and paper. Say each of the words listed below, one at a time. Ask your child to listen to the consonant sounds at the <u>beginning</u> of each word and have him or her write the <u>two</u> letters with which each word begins. (The answers are underlined here.)

<u>br</u>ush   <u>dr</u>ive   <u>gr</u>eat   <u>fr</u>eeze   <u>sl</u>ed   <u>tr</u>ap   <u>sk</u>ate   <u>sm</u>all

<u>pl</u>ay   <u>fl</u>ood   <u>gl</u>ass   <u>cl</u>ean   <u>sp</u>eed   <u>cr</u>ush   <u>bl</u>ind   <u>st</u>ack

2. Print the word *car* on a piece of paper and underline the letters *ar*. Say the word *car* and ask your child to listen to the sound the letters *ar* stand for. Then ask if she or he can name other words with the same sound. Write each word your child suggests and have him or her underline the letters *ar* in each word. You may wish to repeat the same activity with the word *for* and the letters *or*.

Sincerely,

_____

Teacher

HOLT BASIC READING, Workbook, *A Time for Friends*, Unit 3
Parent Component   Holt, Rinehart and Winston, Publishers

Your child was introduced to the words below in Unit 3 of *A Time for Friends*. For home practice, you may wish to print each word on individual 3" × 5" pieces of paper, oaktag, or index cards. When your child can read quickly each of the words, try putting several words together to form a phrase, sentence, or question, for example, "Carmen's special treehouse" or "Mrs. O'Hara heard something walking."

anything	Edwards	never	stood
anywhere	eyes	nut	story
apple	everything		Sunday
aren't		off	Sundays
as	family	oh	
	far	only	there's
beautiful	father	our	think
bedroom	forest		tick
bee		Pablo	tiger
been	gave	Pablo's	tigers
Ben	George	page	toad
best		painted	tock
bite	hand	paints	tonight
Bobby	heard	pink	took
Bobby's	hole	please	toys
boxes		putting	treehouse
Browns	I've		trip
bunny		reached	
	kangaroos	real	walking
camel	knows	rook	Washington
Carmen		rooms	Washingtons
Carmen's	last		way
cherry	light	same	what's
climbed	lights	showed	wherever
clock	log	sitting	whirl
coming	long	smelled	wouldn't
		something	
Daddy's	men	somewhere	zoo
Dan	mole	soon	
dark	monkey's	special	
days	monument	squirrel's	
D.C.	most	state	
doors	motel		
	moving		
	Mrs. O'Hara		

HOLT BASIC READING, Workbook, *A Time for Friends,* Unit 3
Parent Component   Holt, Rinehart and Winston, Publishers

Have your child read each word in the boxes on the back of this page aloud. If the word contains the short *a* vowel sound (as in *bat*), the child should color the box red. If the word contains the long *a* vowel sound (as in *make*), the child should color the box blue.

When all the boxes have been colored, the child should see a number. Explain that Carmen's cat has just had kittens, and that this number will tell how many kittens there are. Have your child write the number in the sentence below the game. Then ask the child to read the sentence to you.

Answers: The red number that should appear is 4. To show the correct answer, the words should be colored as follows:

Red Words (short *a* vowel sound)		Blue Words (long *a* vowel sound)	
bad	as	take	page
crab	last	wait	paint
sat	trap	save	stage
hats	cat	gave	cave
Dan	hand	same	state

"Carmen's New Kittens"

bad	take	as	paint
crab	wait	last	stage
sat	hats	Dan	hand
save	same	trap	cave
gave	page	cat	state

Carmen's cat has _____ new kittens.

HOLT BASIC READING, Workbook, *A Time for Friends*, Unit 3
Parent Component   Holt, Rinehart and Winston, Publishers

"A New Home for Mrs. O'Hara"

Mrs. O'Hara was moving.
But she wasn't moving to a real house.
Mrs. O'Hara was a monkey.
And she was moving to a zoo.

Mrs. O'Hara had lived with the Browns.
Bobby Brown loved Mrs. O'Hara.
But now Mrs. O'Hara was too big.
She liked to climb and bite the cat.
"If only Mrs. O'Hara didn't bite," said Bobby.
"Then she wouldn't have to go to the zoo."

One afternoon some men came to Bobby's house.
They came to take Mrs. O'Hara to the zoo.
The men put the monkey in a special box.
"Good-by, Mrs. O'Hara," called Bobby.

One Sunday the Browns went to the zoo.
They saw a camel.
They saw a beautiful tiger.
And they saw Mrs. O'Hara!

Mrs. O'Hara had lots of monkeys to play with.
She was happy.
"This is the best place for Mrs. O'Hara,"
thought Bobby.
Now Bobby was happy, too.

Note to parent: After your child has read the story, have him/her read each question below and circle the correct answer. Answers are on page 105.

---

1. Who was Mrs. O'Hara?

   a woman   a monkey   a mole

2. Where had Mrs. O'Hara lived?

   with the Browns   with Bobby's cousin

   with Carmen

3. Where was Mrs. O'Hara moving?

   to Washington   to a motel   to the zoo

4. Where did the moving men put Mrs. O'Hara?

   in a room   in a treehouse   in a special box

5. When did the Browns go to the zoo?

   at night   on Sunday   in winter

HOLT BASIC READING, Workbook, *A Time for Friends*, Unit 3
Parent Component   Holt, Rinehart and Winston, Publishers